🖐 Contents

 # To the Teacher

This is one in a series of hands-on science activity books for middle school and early high school students. A recent national survey of middle school students conducted by the National Science Foundation (NSF) found that

- more than half listed science as their favorite subject.
- more than half wanted more hands-on activities.
- 90 percent stated the best way for them to learn science was to do experiments themselves.

The books in this series seek to capitalize on that NSF survey. The books are not texts but supplements. They offer hands-on, fun activities that will turn some students on to science. You and your students should select which activities are to be carried out. All of the activities need not be done. Pick and choose those activities that best meet the needs of your students. All of these activities can be done in school, and some can be done at home. The authors are teachers, and the activities have been field tested in a public middle school and/or high school.

Students will need only basic, standard scientific equipment that can be found in most middle and high school science laboratories. The activities range from the simple (looking at optical illusions) to the difficult (measuring expiratory reserve volume). There is something for every student.

THE ACTIVITIES CAN BE USED:

- to provide hands-on experiences pertaining to textbook content.
- to give verbally limited children a chance to succeed and gain extra credit.
- as the basis for class or school science fair projects or for other science competitions.
- to involve students in science club undertakings.
- as homework assignments.
- to involve parents in their child's science education and experiences.
- to foster an appreciation of the relationships between nutrition, the mind, and the body.

Students can learn important scientific principles from carrying out these activities. For example:

- Sensations may be complex rather than simple. Multiple sensations can produce a single consequence. Activities 14, 15, and 16, for example, explore the components of the sensation of taste.
- Mathematics, science, and technology are interwoven in some of the nutrition activities (for example, Activity 12: Milk, Hot Dogs, and Nutritional Math).

Each activity has a Teacher Resource section that includes, besides helpful hints and suggestions, a scoring rubric, quiz questions, and Internet connections for those students who wish to go further and carry out the follow-up activities. Instructional objectives and the National Science Standards that apply to each activity are provided to help you meet state and local expectations.

Walch Hands-on Science Series

Nutrition, Mind, and Body

by Joel Beller and Carl Raab

illustrated by Lloyd Birmingham

J. WESTON

WALCH
PUBLISHER

Portland, Maine

User's Guide
to
Walch Reproducible Books

As part of our general effort to provide educational materials that are as practical and economical as possible, we have designated this publication a "reproducible book." The designation means that purchase of the book includes purchase of the right to limited reproduction of all pages on which this symbol appears:

Here is the basic Walch policy: We grant to individual purchasers of this book the right to make sufficient copies of reproducible pages for use by all students of a single teacher. This permission is limited to a single teacher and does not apply to entire schools or school systems, so institutions purchasing the book should pass the permission on to a single teacher. Copying of the book or its parts for resale is prohibited.

Any questions regarding this policy or requests to purchase further reproduction rights should be addressed to:

Permissions Editor
J. Weston Walch, Publisher
321 Valley Street • P. O. Box 658
Portland, Maine 04104-0658

1   2   3   4   5   6   7   8   9   10
ISBN 0-8251-3759-4

Seeing Can Be Deceiving!—Part 1

✔ INSTRUCTIONAL OBJECTIVES

Students will be able to

- record and analyze data.
- draw conclusions based upon data.
- explain how afterimages are formed.
- create their own optical illusions.

🌐 NATIONAL SCIENCE STANDARDS ADDRESSED

Students demonstrate an understanding of

- response to stimuli.
- senses and behavior.
- big ideas and unifying concepts, such as cause and effect.

Students demonstrate scientific inquiry and problem-solving skills by

- distinguishing causes and effects.
- identifying problems.
- working individually and in teams to collect and share information.

✂ MATERIALS

- Two toothpicks
- Corrugated cardboard strip measuring at least 25 cm by 25 cm
- Glue stick or white liquid glue for paper
- Scissors
- Two sheets of $8\frac{1}{2}$" × 11" white paper
- Two half-dollars or quarters
- Two glass stirring rods or thin wooden dowels
- Bright red and light green $\frac{3}{4}$" stickers
- Crayons or paints and brushes
- Round bottle whose base measures 10 cm or more in diameter
- Pencil
- Metric ruler
- Stopwatch

💻 INTERNET TIE-INS

http://www.yorku.ca/eye/thejoy.htm
http://psych.hanover.edu/Krantz/BenhamTop/background.html
http://www.phs.princeton.k12.oh.us/Public/Lessons/opt.html
http://www.yahoo.com/Entertainment/Miscellaneous/Optical_Ill.

❓ QUIZ

1. Motion pictures consist of a series of still-picture frames. Why do they show motion when passed through a motion picture projector?
2. What is the function of the cone cells of the retina?
3. What are some causes of optical illusions?

HELPFUL HINTS AND DISCUSSION

Time frame: One class period
Structure: Individually or in cooperative learning groups
Location: In class or at home

Discuss with the students (a) color vision, motion vision, and optical illusions based on afterimages, and (b) persistence of vision. The discussion should include cone cells in the retina.

ADAPTATIONS FOR HIGH AND LOW ACHIEVERS

High Achievers: These students should be encouraged to carry out the follow-up investigations. They also should help the low achievers describe what they see in order to fill in the Data Collection and Analysis section and answer the Concluding Questions.

Low Achievers: You and the high achievers should help the low achievers understand the concepts of optical illusions and their causes. You should also help the low achievers draw the American flag with the colors specified.

SCORING RUBRIC

Full credit should be given to those students who record observations and who provide correct answers in full sentences. Extra credit can be given if any of the Follow-up Activities are completed.

toothpick — cardboard — toothpick

Seeing Can Be Deceiving!—Part 1

👆 BEFORE YOU BEGIN 👆

No, the title of this activity should not be "Seeing Is Believing!" In this activity, you and the members of your group will investigate **optical illusions**. Optical illusions result when your eyes and brain fool you about what you see.

In the first part of this activity, you will investigate **persistence of vision**, which means that an image remains in your eye for about $\frac{1}{50}$th of a second. In other words, if you add a new image before the $\frac{1}{50}$th of a second is up, you will see both images at the same time. You will also explore what happens when your **cone cells,** which are sensitive to certain colors of light, become overstimulated. The result is **afterimages**, which occur when you then stare at a white sheet of paper.

✂ MATERIALS

- Two toothpicks
- Corrugated cardboard strip measuring at least 25 cm by 25 cm
- Glue stick or white liquid glue for paper
- Scissors
- Two sheets of $8\frac{1}{2}$" × 11" white paper
- Two half-dollars or quarters
- Two glass stirring rods or thin wooden dowels

- Bright red and light green $\frac{3}{4}$" stickers
- Crayons or paints and brushes
- Round bottle whose base measures 10 cm or more in diameter
- Pencil
- Metric ruler
- Stopwatch

📦 PROCEDURE

1. Using the bottle as a template, cut out a circular piece of the corrugated cardboard. If the cardboard is not white, cover the disk of cardboard on both sides with white paper. Use glue to cement the paper onto the cardboard.

2. Make a pencil mark about 1 cm from the end of each toothpick. Coat each toothpick with glue up to the 1-cm mark.

3. Use the ruler to find the diameter of the disk. Using the pencil, mark the diameter. Then, insert the toothpicks into the corrugated cardboard, one at each end of the diameter, up to the 1-cm mark. Let the glue dry. Your creation should look like Diagram 1.

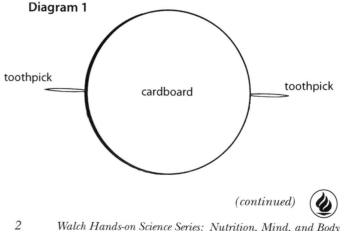

Diagram 1

toothpick · cardboard · toothpick

(continued)

Seeing Can Be Deceiving!—Part 1 *(continued)*

4. Cut out the pictures of the cooked lobster and the plate found below. Color the lobster red, using crayons or paint; then paste the lobster on one side of the cardboard, making sure to center it. In the center on the other side of the cardboard circle, paste the picture of the plate and utensils. Hold the disk by its toothpick handles, and slowly twirl the disk back and forth. In the Data Collection and Analysis section, describe what you see. Now, twirl the disk quickly. Record in the Data Collection and Analysis section what happens to the images when they are twirled quickly.

5. Another illusion that is based upon the persistence of vision is to visualize three coins when, in reality, there are only two. Place two quarters between your left and right index fingers as shown in Diagram 2. (If you are using half-dollar coins or if your fingers are small, it may be easier to use your thumbs.) Slide your fingers back and forth **quickly**. Describe in the Data Collection and Analysis section what your team members see as you do this.

Diagram 2

6. Place your red sticker in the space provided below. Stare at the sticker for 30 seconds; then shift your gaze quickly to the white sticker in the center. In the Data Collection and Analysis section, describe what you see.

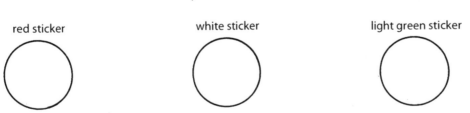

red sticker   white sticker   light green sticker

7. What you see is called an **afterimage**. This occurs when the cells in the **retina** of your eye, called **cones**, become overstimulated; they can no longer see colors to which they normally are sensitive. You have three types of cone cells: one type is sensitive only to red light, the second is sensitive only to blue light, and the third is sensitive only to green light. After you have stared at the

(continued)

red dot for a long time, the red-sensitive cone cells in your eye become fatigued; when you look at the white sticker (which is made up of all colors of the spectrum), you see an afterimage of the sticker in all colors **except red**, because the cone cells that see red are too tired to function.

8. Repeat what you did in step 6 with the light green sticker. In the Data Collection and Analysis section, describe what you see.

9. Using your crayons or paints, draw an American flag in the space below. However, make the colors **cyan** (bright blue) for red stripes, **black** for the white stars and white stripes, and **yellow** for the blue background of the stars. Stare at the flag for 20 to 30 seconds; then look at the white rectangle next to it.

Draw your flag here:

10. In the Data Collection and Analysis section, describe the flag as you see it in the rectangle above.

DATA COLLECTION AND ANALYSIS

1. Describe what you saw when you rapidly twirled the disk with the lobster on one side and the plate on the other. _____

_____

_____

2. Explain what you observed when you moved the two coins rapidly between your fingers. _____

_____

_____

3. In the circle on the right, fill in the color or colors you saw after staring at the red dot.

(continued)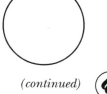

Seeing Can Be Deceiving!—Part 1 *(continued)*

4. In the circle on the right, fill in the color or colors you saw after staring at the light green dot.

5. What did your flag look like as an afterimage? _____

_____

_____

❓ CONCLUDING QUESTIONS

1. Which type of illusion was the most interesting to you? Why? _____

_____

_____

_____

2. Why do scientists rely on optical instruments more than their eyes in order to gain scientific information?

_____

_____

_____

_____

3. Explain the terms **optical illusion**, **persistence of vision**, and **afterimage**. Discuss why these occur.

_____

_____

_____

_____

👁 Follow-up Activities 👁

1. Using the library or the Internet, research "black and white interference."

2. Design an optical illusion based upon "after vision."

3. Prepare a book containing a series of related pictures stapled together. When the pages are flipped, the viewer should see an action movie, such as a bird flying or a dog running.

✔️ INSTRUCTIONAL OBJECTIVES

Students will be able to

- record and analyze data.
- draw conclusions based upon data.
- explain the importance of three-dimensional vision.
- create their own optical illusions.

🌐 NATIONAL SCIENCE STANDARDS ADDRESSED

Students demonstrate an understanding of

- response to stimuli.
- senses and behavior.
- big ideas and unifying concepts, such as cause and effect.

Students demonstrate scientific inquiry and problem-solving skills by

- distinguishing causes and effects.
- identifying problems.
- working in teams to collect and share information.

Students demonstrate effective scientific communication by

- using data to resolve disagreements.

 MATERIALS

- Two chairs
- Desk or table
- 8½" × 11" paper

HELPFUL HINTS AND DISCUSSION

Time frame:	One class period
Structure:	In cooperative learning groups
Location:	In class or at home

Discuss the difficulties that people who have lost an eye have in dealing with depth perception. Also discuss the fact that people can measure distances more effectively with two eyes than with one. It is important to emphasize that the brain merges images from each eye into one composite image.

ADAPTATIONS FOR HIGH AND LOW ACHIEVERS

High Achievers: These students should assist the low achievers in describing what they see in order to complete the Data Collection and Analysis section. These students should answer everything in the Concluding Questions and perform most or all exercises in the Follow-up Activities, especially the last one.

Low Achievers: The high achievers should help the low achievers with positioning their forefingers properly in front of their eyes.

SCORING RUBRIC

Full credit should be given to those students who record observations and who provide correct answers in full sentences to the questions. Extra credit can be given if any of the Follow-up Activities are completed.

🖥️ INTERNET TIE-INS

http://www.vision3d.com.
http://www.eyenet.org/public/museum/circles.html

QUIZ

1. What are the advantages of three-dimensional vision?
2. What are some occupations that depend upon three-dimensional vision?

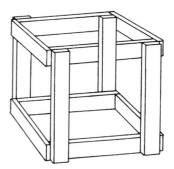

Seeing Can Be Deceiving!—Part 2

☞ BEFORE YOU BEGIN ☜

Your brain and eyes work together to create what you see. You normally see things in three dimensions; your brain gets clues about the depth, position, and shading of what you are looking at. If you look at a two-dimensional object, the images sent to the brain may lack some of these features so that the images look flat.

In this activity, you will explore ways in which seeing three-dimensional objects two-dimensionally can fool your brain.

✂ MATERIALS

- Two chairs
- Table or desk
- $8\frac{1}{2}$" × 11" paper

📐 PROCEDURE

1. You have two eyes separated from each other by your nose. When you look at any object, each eye sees the object from a slightly different angle. Thus, each view is slightly different. Look at any distant object—a chart on the wall, a picture, or another object—alternately covering each eye so that you see with one eye at a time. You should see the same object with each eye, but with a slightly different view. When you look with both eyes simultaneously, both views arrive in the brain at the same time, and the brain will combine both views into one three-dimensional or **stereoscopic** image. To illustrate further, do the following:

   (a) Put both forefingers together, fingertip to fingertip. Raise your hands so that they are about 8 cm in front of your face and are in line with the tip of your nose. Both fingers should be parallel to the floor. Slowly raise  both hands, keeping your forefingers together, until they are directly in front of your eyes. Keep both eyes open, and very slowly move your forefingers apart approximately 1 cm. Look for a tiny, football-shaped finger with a fingernail at each end. This effect is due, in part, to the fact that part of the image seen by the left eye and part of the image seen by the right eye overlap and fuse. If you hold your fingers farther away from your nose, no overlapping and fusing of images will occur. Try it!

   (b) Now, wiggle your forefingers up and down. In the Data Collection and Analysis section, questions 1 and 2, describe what you see.

   (c) Next, close your left eye. What do you see? Open the left eye and close the right. How does what you see compare with what you saw with the left eye closed? Write your answer in the Data Collection and Analysis section, questions 3 and 4.

2. Take a piece of $8\frac{1}{2}$" × 11" paper and roll it into a tube lengthwise. Hold the tube in your right hand and point the tube toward the floor. Place your left hand on the tube with the palm facing you. Keep both eyes open. Move your left hand slowly toward and then away from your eyes.

(continued) 🔥

Seeing Can Be Deceiving!—Part 2 *(continued)*

Where did the hole in your hand come from? Record your answer in the Data Collection and Analysis section, question 5.

3. In order to perform tasks that require three-dimensional vision, you must keep both eyes open. To prove this, do the following. You and a member of a cooperative learning team should sit in chairs on opposite sides of a desk or table. Use the palm of one hand to cover one eye. Keep both eyes open.

4. Each team member is to extend the index finger of the hand not covering the eye and **quickly** try to touch the tip of the index finger of the other person. Try this only once or twice. Then switch, by covering the other eye and using the other hand. Remember to extend the index finger toward the other person's index finger. Try this twice. Record the results in the Data Collection and Analysis section. Repeat steps 3 and 4 without covering one eye. Record the results in the Data Collection and Analysis section.

DATA COLLECTION AND ANALYSIS

1. Describe what you saw when your forefingers were together and both eyes were open.

   _____

   _____

2. What did you see when you wiggled your fingers? _____

   _____

   _____

3. What did you see with the left eye closed? _____

   _____

4. How did what you saw with the right eye closed compare with what you saw with the left eye closed?

   _____

   _____

5. Why did your hand appear to have a hole in it? _____

   _____

   _____

6. Of the four attempts to touch the tips of the index fingers with one eye covered, how many attempts were successful? _____

7. Of the four attempts to touch the tips of the index fingers with both eyes uncovered, how many attempts were successful? _____

(continued)

Seeing Can Be Deceiving!—Part 2 *(continued)*

❓ CONCLUDING QUESTIONS

1. What are some tasks besides catching a ball that require three-dimensional vision?

   _____

   _____

   _____

   _____

2. Why is three-dimensional vision in humans and animals important for survival?

   _____

   _____

   _____

   _____

 **Follow-up Activities**

1. Research binocular vision and report your findings to the class.

2. Investigate in the library and on the World Wide Web how to view in three dimensions without the use of special glasses that have one red lens and one blue lens.

3. Investigate and possibly create drawings of things that cannot exist, such as the object below.

Can Eating Ice Cream Be Painful?

✔ INSTRUCTIONAL OBJECTIVES

Students will be able to

- test a hypothesis.
- record and analyze data.
- plan and conduct a controlled experiment.
- draw conclusions based upon data.
- state the importance of negative conclusions in a scientific experiment.
- use appropriate techniques to gather data.

🌐 NATIONAL SCIENCE STANDARDS ADDRESSED

Students demonstrate an understanding of

- response to environmental stimuli.
- senses and behavior.
- big ideas and unifying concepts, such as cause and effect.
- impacts of technology, such as benefits and risks.

Students demonstrate scientific inquiry and problem-solving skills by

- framing questions to distinguish cause and effect.
- identifying problems.
- proposing, recognizing, and considering alternative explanations.
- working individually and in teams to collect and share information.

Students demonstrate effective scientific communication by

- communicating in a form suited to the purpose by using data to resolve disagreements.
- representing data in multiple ways.
- explaining scientific concepts to others.

✂ MATERIALS

- Two dozen disposable plastic tablespoons
- Thermometer
- Frozen ice cream
- Stopwatch, or any time piece with a second hand

💻 INTERNET TIE-INS

http://204.27.188.70/daily/01-97/01-26-97/zzzaddon.htm
http://www.freep.com/news/health/qnew13.htm

❓ QUIZ

1. Explain why the results of an experiment would be considered unreliable if you used only one subject.
2. What is the relationship between an uncomfortable feeling experienced when eating and making food choices?

HELPFUL HINTS AND DISCUSSION

Time frame: One to two weeks
Structure: Individually or in cooperative learning groups
Location: In class, at home, and with neighbors

The only safety consideration is that different, clean spoons be used for each subject. It is very important that the ice cream be frozen (the air temperature must be at 27°C or higher) and that the ice cream be held **in the back of the mouth** until it melts.

ADAPTATIONS FOR HIGH AND LOW ACHIEVERS

High Achievers: These students should be encouraged to carry out Follow-up Activities 3 and 6.

Low Achievers: If these students have trouble using a stopwatch, they should be told to count slowly up to 30. These students should be required to work in cooperative learning groups composed of a mix of high and low achievers. Another possibility is to carry out this activity with the help of an educational aide or a parent.

SCORING RUBRIC

Full credit should be given to those students who record observations and who provide correct answers in full sentences to the questions. Extra credit can be given if any of the Follow-up Activities are completed.

Can Eating Ice Cream Be Painful?

👋 BEFORE YOU BEGIN 👋

Some people develop a dislike for certain foods based upon uncomfortable or negative experiences. Likes and dislikes affect the food choices of most people. Would you be surprised to learn that approximately one third of the population suffer a severe stabbing head pain that lasts a few seconds after eating ice cream? Have you ever experienced this? There are several theories as to the cause of ice cream headaches; but as of this writing, no definite cause has been determined.

A medical researcher has reported that headaches can occur after eating ice cream if three conditions are met:

1. The ice cream is very cold.
2. The air temperature is hot.
3. The ice cream is held in the **back of the mouth** until it melts.

Would you like to test these findings? This could be a fun investigation. After all, you could eat all the leftover ice cream, even if your results were negative. This brings up an important point. When testing a scientist's hypothesis, **negative results are just as important as proving that the researcher's hypothesis is correct**. After testing this hypothesis on yourself and your classmates, you can use members of your family, neighbors, and friends. You should use a minimum of 10 subjects. Twenty-five would be even better. When testing a hypothesis, the more subjects used, the more reliable and valid are the results.

✂ MATERIALS

- Two dozen disposable plastic tablespoons
- Thermometer
- Frozen ice cream
- Stopwatch, or any time piece with a second hand

📓 PROCEDURE

You can research this problem with another student in a cooperative learning team, or it can be done by you alone. Every subject, including you, must be treated the same way in order to keep the variables to a minimum. Each subject should receive the same instructions, the same amount of frozen ice cream, and so on. You might want to use the instructions printed below.

Suggested Instructions to Subjects

"Some people find that eating ice cream on a warm day is a painful experience. I would like you to help me find out if this is true or not. I would like to use you as a test subject. All you have to do is place a spoonful of solid ice cream at the back of your mouth and keep it there until it melts. Then swallow it. Report any unusual sensations that you experience within 30 seconds after the ice cream is positioned in the back of your mouth. Do you have any questions? Now, here is a spoonful of ice cream. Try it! **Remember: Don't swallow the ice cream until it has melted! Be sure to tell me if you feel any discomfort.**"

Make sure that every subject follows the same procedure. Complete the data table in the Data Collection and Analysis section.

(continued)

Can Eating Ice Cream Be Painful? *(continued)*

DATA COLLECTION AND ANALYSIS

Name of Subject	Age	Sex	Date of Test	Air Temperature (Degrees C)	No Discomfort or Headache (Describe)

When you find a subject who does report a headache, ask that person if you could use him or her for further testing.

1. Based upon your data, what percentage of your subjects suffer from ice cream headaches?

_____

2. Did your data indicate a relationship between age and ice cream headaches? Gender (male or female) and ice cream headaches? Explain your answers.

_____

_____

_____

CONCLUDING QUESTIONS

1. Do research in the library or on the Internet to find other foods that cause unpleasant eating experiences.
2. Write a report about food allergies and present it to your class as a follow-up to this activity.

(continued)

Can Eating Ice Cream Be Painful? *(continued)*

👌 Follow-up Activities 👌

1. Ask the subjects to keep the ice cream on the side, rather than in the back, of their mouths. Are any headaches reported? What other variables might affect the outcome?
2. Repeat the original experiment on a cool day or in a cold air-conditioned room. Do the results differ?
3. Determine if this trait is inherited by testing family members of those subjects who reported that they felt discomfort after being tested.
4. Substitute sorbet for ice cream. What are the results? (Hint: If frozen ice cream causes headaches and sorbet does not, the cause may be one or more of the ingredients in the ice cream.)
5. Determine if subjects get a headache from diet ice cream or only from regular ice cream.
6. Design an experiment to determine the minimal difference between the ice cream temperature (assume it is 0°C) and the air temperature that triggers a response.

What Parts of the Body Are Involved in Maintaining Balance?

✔ INSTRUCTIONAL OBJECTIVES

Students will be able to

- record and analyze data.
- conduct an experiment.
- draw conclusions based upon data.

🌐 NATIONAL SCIENCE STANDARDS ADDRESSED

Students demonstrate an understanding of

- response to environmental stimuli.
- senses and behavior.
- big ideas and unifying concepts, such as cause and effect.

Students demonstrate scientific inquiry and problem-solving skills by

- distinguishing causes and effects.
- identifying problems.
- working in teams to collect and share information.

Students demonstrate effective scientific communication by

- representing data in multiple ways.
- explaining scientific concepts to others.

 MATERIALS

- Six swivel chairs
- Stopwatch

HELPFUL HINTS AND DISCUSSION

Time frame: One period
Structure: In cooperative learning groups
Location: In class

✋ **Note: This activity requires adult supervision.** It would be wise to explain this activity to the students, especially the roles of the timekeeper/leader, recordkeeper, and the subjects. Students should initially work in groups of eight. The successful subjects should combine after the first trial to provide an adequate test group. Point out the need for the subjects to be honest—that is, to keep their eyes closed at the proper times and to admit when they failed to keep their feet off the ground. Stress that this is a scientific experiment involving balance, vision, and equilibrium. Demonstrate how students should sit in the swivel chairs and how fast the assistant record keepers should spin the chairs. You may wish to combine Tasks 1 and 2 into a single task with a control and an experimental group. However, it is advisable to move only those who were able to overcome the obstacle of lack of vision on to Task 3 (the swivel chair).

ADAPTATIONS FOR HIGH AND LOW ACHIEVERS

High Achievers: These students should be encouraged to carry out Follow-up Activities 3 and 6.

Low Achievers: None of these students should be selected to be the timekeeper/leader. They should work with the high achievers in filling in the data table.

SCORING RUBRIC

Full credit should be given to those students who accurately record observations and who provide correct answers in full sentences to the questions. Extra credit can be given if any of the Follow-up Activities are completed.

🖥 INTERNET TIE-INS

http://www.bonus.com8080/contour/neuroscienceforkids@@
http://www.psynt.iupui.edu/kjohnson/S3CON.html.
http://weber.u.washington.edu/chudler/interr.html

❓ QUIZ

1. Which parts of the body are involved when a person becomes "seasick"?
2. Why are people who get seasick advised to look at the horizon?

What Parts of the Body Are Involved in Maintaining Balance?

🖐 BEFORE YOU BEGIN 🖐

In this activity, you and members of your group will investigate the factors that allow you to maintain your balance. You will further investigate which of these factors is most important. The parts of your body that play a role in maintaining balance include the **cerebellum** of the brain, the **semicircular canals** in the inner ear, and the **eyes**.

This activity should be carried out with groups of eight students. It is important to remember that this is not a contest but a scientific investigation. **Honesty is most important** to ensure that the results are meaningful.

✂ MATERIALS

- Six swivel chairs
- Stopwatch

🖐 Note: **Do not do any of the following activities without adult supervision!**

PROCEDURE

1. For each group of eight, appoint one member of the group as the timekeeper/leader and another as the recordkeeper. The other six students will become subjects. Clear an area of the classroom so that the six subjects can stand in a straight line and face the timekeeper/leader and the record keeper.

2. In the table in the Data Collection and Analysis section, record the number of subjects.

3. Have the timekeeper/leader explain to the subjects that, for this task (Task 1), they are going to stand on one leg for 30 seconds without holding on to anything for support. They are to begin at the signal. They can stand on either the left or right foot and may move their arms, but they should remain standing in one place without hopping around. Their eyes should be open.

4. At the signal from the timekeeper, the subjects should stand on the foot of their choice. The recordkeeper should watch the subjects to see if anyone puts a foot down or hops instead of standing. The recordkeeper should then tally the number of subjects who complete the task successfully. The subjects who were unable to keep their balance should assist the recordkeeper and watch the remaining subjects perform the next task.

5. After a brief rest, the remaining subjects from all the groups in the class should line up again and should repeat the previous procedure, *except* that this time, for Task 2, they are to keep *both eyes closed* while keeping one foot off the ground. A new recordkeeper and some assistants should be appointed to watch for those who can't maintain their balance and remain in one place on one foot. The number of successful subjects is to be recorded in the data table. Subjects should compare their sensations and difficulties in doing Task 2 with their sensations and difficulties in Task 1. Record this information in the Data Collection and Analysis section.

(continued) 🔥

What Parts of the Body Are Involved in Maintaining Balance? *(continued)*

6. After a brief rest, those who completed the second task successfully should be seated in swivel chairs for Task 3. The timekeeper/leader will assign an assistant record keeper to each swivel chair. At the command of the timekeeper, the assistants are to spin the subjects in the chairs around five times. The spinning should be done quickly, but not so fast that the seated subjects are in danger of falling off the chairs. Immediately after being spun, each subject is to stand on one foot with eyes closed for 30 seconds. Again, the recordkeeper and the assistants are to observe the actions of the subjects, checking to be sure that the subjects keep their eyes closed and that each subject keeps one foot off the floor. The subjects should compare their sensations and difficulties in doing this task with the sensations and difficulties of Task2 . Complete the table in the Data Collection and Analysis section.

DATA COLLECTION AND ANALYSIS

Number of subjects _____

Task	Number of Successful Subjects	Percent Successful	Sensations and Difficulties
1			
2			
3			

1. Based upon your data, what is the effect of vision upon maintaining one's balance? _____

_____

_____

2. Why was it more difficult to maintain one's balance during Task 3 than during Task 2? _____

_____

CONCLUDING QUESTIONS

1. Which is more important for maintaining balance: vision or equilibrium? Explain your answer on the back of this sheet.

2. Research in the library and report to the class which parts of the body are involved in maintaining balance. Explain the role of each part.

👆 Follow-up Activities 👆

1. In the library or on the Internet, research "tracking reflexes" and equilibrium reflexes.
2. Design an experiment to investigate how a tracking reflex helps you focus on a moving object.

How Much Water Does a Popcorn Kernel Contain?

✓ INSTRUCTIONAL OBJECTIVES

Students will be able to

- record and analyze data.
- draw conclusions based upon data.
- explain the reasons why popping corn pops and other seeds do not pop.
- determine the amount of water in a kernel of popcorn.

🌐 NATIONAL SCIENCE STANDARDS ADDRESSED

Students demonstrate an understanding of

- transfer of energy.
- structure of living things.
- big ideas and unifying concepts, such as cause and effect.

Students demonstrate scientific inquiry and problem-solving skills by

- distinguishing causes and effects.
- identifying problems.
- working in teams to collect data.

Students demonstrate effective scientific communication by

- representing data in multiple ways.

✂ MATERIALS

- One pint-size jar (or larger) with screw-on cover
- Water
- One-half cup of corn kernels
- ✋Hot-air popcorn maker
- Plastic bag (1 qt.) that can be tightly sealed (large enough to collect 25 popped corn kernels)
- Triple-beam balance
- Paper towel
- Teaspoon

✋ = Safety icon

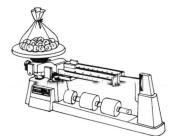

HELPFUL HINTS AND DISCUSSION

Time frame: Three to four days for preparation of the kernels; one to two periods for the activity itself.

Structure: In cooperative learning groups of two to four students

Location: In class

A hot-air popcorn maker is suggested because it is the safest way to make popcorn. **Students should be cautioned against touching the popcorn maker until it has had a chance to cool down.** Students are advised to seal the plastic bag containing the popcorn as quickly as possible. Popped corn will absorb moisture from the air quickly, especially if the humidity is high. The preparation requires three or four days. During this time the corn kernels are placed in a sealed jar containing a half teaspoon of water. The purpose is to allow the kernels to absorb water, which is essential for popping. Carrying out this preparation procedure will increase the number of kernels that will pop.

It would be wise for the teacher to review with students the rationale of this activity, the measurements that will be made, and the columns in the data table.

ADAPTATIONS FOR HIGH AND LOW ACHIEVERS

High Achievers: These students should be encouraged to carry out Follow-up Activities. They also should assist the low achievers with carrying out this activity and collecting and analyzing the data.

Low Achievers: These students should be helped in completing the data table and in carrying out the averages and other mathematical tasks.

SCORING RUBRIC

Full credit should be given to those students who record the data and who do the mathematics correctly. They also should answer all of the concluding questions. Extra credit can be given if any of the Follow-up Activities are completed.

**INTERNET TIE-INS**   http://chemwww.byu.edu/classes/chem/1052/doc/popcorn.html
http://www.point-and-click.com.kids/popcorn.html
http://athena.wednet.edu/curric/weather/adoptcty/popcorn.html

QUIZ   1. Why does popcorn pop?
2. What is the relationship between the volume of water in a corn kernel and the volume of steam produced when it is heated?

How Much Water Does a Popcorn Kernel Contain?

✋ BEFORE YOU BEGIN ✋

Like all seeds, corn kernels—including the type used for popcorn—contain water. In order for the popcorn kernels to pop, the water inside them must be changed to steam. But, since all seeds contain water, why can't you pop barley or sunflower seeds? The reason is that popcorn kernels have a very tough outer coat called the **pericarp**. Sunflower seeds and other seeds have a pericarp, but it doesn't compare in strength to the pericarp of corn kernels. In this activity, you will discover how much water is inside a kernel of popcorn.

You may have noticed that not all the kernels pop when you make popcorn. The main reason for the failure to pop is that water was lost from these kernels when they were stored. This is because the water evaporated from these kernels when they were exposed to the air. Your first task will be to replace any lost water from the kernels so that as many as possible will pop when placed in the hot-air popcorn maker. Start this process three to four days before you begin this activity. Place a half cup of corn kernels into the jar and add a half teaspoon of water. Close the jar tightly. Shake up the contents of the jar for a minute or two in order to mix the water and the kernels. Set the jar aside in a safe place until you are ready to start this activity.

✂ MATERIALS

- One pint-size jar (or larger) with screw-on cover
- Water
- One-half cup of corn kernels
- ✋ Hot-air popcorn maker
- Plastic bag (1 qt.) that can be tightly sealed (large enough to collect 25 popped corn kernels)

- Triple-beam balance
- Paper towel
- Teaspoon

✋ = Safety icon

PROCEDURE

1. Remove the kernels from the moisturizing jar. Use a piece of paper towel to dry the kernels thoroughly.

2. Place 25 kernels on the balance and weigh them. Record the weight in grams (g), to the nearest 0.1 g, in the Data Collection and Analysis section.

3. Weigh the plastic bag that you will use to collect the popcorn. Record the weight to the nearest 0.1 g in the Data Collection and Analysis section.

4. Clean the inside of the popcorn maker well. Place the kernels in the hot-air popper and make popcorn. Place the plastic bag by the outlet chute and collect all the popcorn that is made.

(continued)

How Much Water Does a Popcorn Kernel Contain? *(continued)*

5. When you can no longer hear kernels popping, pour the contents of the plastic bag into a shallow bowl. Remove any unpopped kernels. Return the popcorn, pieces of popcorn, and pieces of pericarp to the plastic bag. Quickly seal the plastic bag to prevent the popcorn from absorbing moisture from the air. **CAUTION: Don't touch any part of the popping machine until it cools down. It can get quite hot!**

6. Count the number of unpopped kernels removed in step 5. Subtract this number from 25, and record this number in line (e) in the Data Collection and Analysis section. Now, weigh these unpopped kernels and record their weight in grams in the space indicated in line (e).

7. Weigh the plastic bag and its contents. Record the weight in line (c) in the Data Collection and Analysis section. Now, subtract the weight of the bag in line (b) from the total weight of the bag plus the popcorn; record this data in line (d).

8. Repeat steps 2 to 7 twice so that you have made three trials.

9. Share the popcorn with your team members and enjoy!

DATA COLLECTION AND ANALYSIS

Trial 1.
(a) 25 unpopped popcorn kernels weigh _____ g.

(b) The empty plastic bag weighs _____ g.

(c) The plastic bag plus (number) _____ kernels of popped corn weigh _____ g.

(d) Weight of (number) _____ popped kernels is _____ g (c − b = d).

(e) Weight of (number) _____ remaining unpopped kernels is _____ .

(f) If some of the original 25 kernels did not pop, you will have to subtract the weight of the unpopped kernels from the original weight of all the kernels before popping. For example, suppose that 20 kernels popped and 5 did not. Assume that the 25 originally weighed 12.5 g. Each kernel weighed an average of 0.5 g. If 5 failed to pop, you would have to deduct 2.5 g, as recorded in line (e), from line (a) in order to compare the weight of equal numbers of popped and unpopped kernels. You will make this comparison by completing the chart on the next page.

(continued)

           Walch Hands-on Science Series: Nutrition, Mind, and Body

How Much Water Does a Popcorn Kernel Contain? *(continued)*

Trial 2. (a) 25 unpopped popcorn kernels weigh _____ g.

(b) The empty plastic bag weighs _____ g.

(c) The plastic bag plus (number) _____ kernels of popped corn weigh _____ g.

(d) Weight of (number) _____ popped kernels is _____ g ($c - b = d$).

(e) Weight of (number) _____ remaining unpopped kernels is _____ g.

(f) If some of the original 25 kernels did not pop, you will have to subtract the weight of the unpopped kernels from the original weight of all the kernels before popping. For example, suppose that 20 kernels popped and 5 did not. Assume that the 25 originally weighed 12.5 g. Each kernel weighed an average of 0.5 g. If 5 failed to pop, you would have to deduct 2.5 g, as recorded in line (e), from line (a) in order to compare the weight of equal numbers of popped and unpopped kernels. You will make this comparison by completing the chart on the next page.

Trial 3. (a) 25 unpopped popcorn kernels weigh _____ g.

(b) The empty plastic bag weighs _____ g.

(c) The plastic bag plus (number) _____ kernels of popped corn weigh _____ g.

(d) Weight of (number) _____ popped kernels is _____ g ($c - b = d$).

(e) Weight of (number) _____ remaining unpopped kernels is _____ g.

(f) If some of the original 25 kernels did not pop, you will have to subtract the weight of the unpopped kernels from the original weight of all the kernels before popping. For example, suppose that 20 kernels popped and 5 did not. Assume that the 25 originally weighed 12.5 g. Each kernel weighed an average of 0.5 g. If 5 failed to pop, you would have to deduct 2.5 g, as recorded in line (e), from line (a) in order to be accurate. Then you will be able to compare the weight of equal numbers of popped and unpopped kernels. You will make this comparison by completing the chart below.

(continued)

How Much Water Does a Popcorn Kernel Contain? *(continued)*

Trial	Weight of Original Kernels with Weight of Unpopped Kernels Subtracted	Weight of Popped Kernels	Difference in Weight Between Unpopped and Popped Kernels (column 2 minus column 3)
1			
2			
3			
Average			

CONCLUDING QUESTIONS

1. Explain why the unpopped kernels weighed more than the popped kernels.
   (**Hint:** Look at the title of this activity.)

   _____

   _____

   _____

2. Calculate the average amount of water in each kernel used in this activity.

   _____

   _____

3. What happened to the steam that made the corn kernels pop? _____

   _____

   _____

Follow-up Activities

1. Repeat this activity, but first break the skin of the pericarp of all 25 kernels by using a fingernail file. How do your results compare with those obtained during the initial activity? How do you explain your results? This should be done under adult supervision.

2. Research how popping corn is harvested and processed. Report your results to the class.

          Walch Hands-on Science Series: Nutrition, Mind, and Body

How Many Calories Are in a Gram of Popcorn?

✓ INSTRUCTIONAL OBJECTIVES

Students will be able to

- record and analyze data.
- draw conclusions based upon data.
- determine the calories in popcorn.
- compare the calories in popcorn with the calories in other snack foods.

🌐 NATIONAL SCIENCE STANDARDS ADDRESSED

Students demonstrate an understanding of

- properties of matter.
- big ideas and unifying concepts, such as cause and effect.
- calories and nutrition.

Students demonstrate scientific inquiry and problem-solving skills by

- using evidence to develop models.
- identifying problems.
- working individually or in teams to collect data.

Students demonstrate competence with the tools of science by

- using scientific equipment.

Students demonstrate scientific competence by

- secondary research, such as using the data of others.

✂ MATERIALS

- Triple-beam balance
- One-half cup of popcorn kernels
- 🖐 Hot-air popcorn maker
- Spatula or scoop
- Bowl to collect the popcorn
- Wire gauze
- Ring stand
- 500-ml heat-resistant beaker
- Burner tripod stand
- 🖐 Matches
- Thermometer
- 120- to 150-ml porcelain evaporating dish
- 250-ml graduated cylinder
- Water
- Safety goggles
- Laboratory apron

 🖐 = Safety icon

HELPFUL HINTS AND DISCUSSION

Time frame: One period
Structure: Individually or in cooperative learning groups
Location: In class or at home

A hot-air popcorn maker is suggested because it is the safest way to make popcorn. **Do not touch the popcorn maker until it has had a chance to cool down. The handling of the matches and the burning of the popcorn must be directly supervised by a teacher or by another adult.** Students should wear goggles and lab aprons when burning the popcorn. It would be prudent to go over the mathematical reasoning involved in this activity.

Discuss the difference between popcorn kernels and popped popcorn.

ADAPTATIONS FOR HIGH AND LOW ACHIEVERS

High Achievers: These students should be encouraged to carry out all the Follow-up Activities. They also should assist the low achievers with carrying out this activity and collecting and analyzing the data.

Low Achievers: These students should be helped with the mathematical tasks and carefully supervised when burning the popcorn.

SCORING RUBRIC

Full credit should be given to those students who record the data correctly and who do the mathematics correctly. They also should answer all of the Concluding Questions. Extra credit can be given if any of the Follow-up Activities are completed.

INTERNET TIE-INS   http://www.actii.com/world.htm.
http://www.kidsweight.com/
http://www.oznet.ksu.edu/ext_f&n/_timely/check.htm

QUIZ   1. Why is popcorn considered an ideal snack food?
2. What are food calories used for in your body?

How Many Calories Are in a Gram of Popcorn?

 BEFORE YOU BEGIN

People today are calorie-conscious because they understand the relationship between calories and weight. The energy found in the foods that we eat, measured in **calories**, fuels our life activities. One calorie is the amount of heat necessary to raise the temperature of one gram of water one degree Celsius. This is a very small amount of heat. The calories that we are familiar with are really measured in **kilocalories**. A kilocalorie is equal to 1,000 calories. When you read a food label that tells you the number of calories in a serving of that food, you are really being told the number of kilocalories that are in one serving.

Scientists assume that the amount of heat produced when food is burned outside the body is equal to the amount of heat produced when that food is oxidized within the body and used for energy.

In this activity, you will measure the number of kilocalories in a serving of popcorn.

MATERIALS

- Triple-beam balance
- One-half cup of popcorn kernels
- Hot-air popcorn maker
- Spatula or scoop
- Bowl to collect the popcorn
- Wire gauze
- Ring stand
- 500-ml heat-resistant beaker

- Burner tripod stand
- Matches
- Thermometer
- 120- to 150-ml porcelain evaporating dish
- 250-ml graduated cylinder
- Water
- Safety goggles
- Laboratory apron

= Safety icon

PROCEDURE

1. Use the hot-air popcorn maker to prepare approximately one-half cup of popcorn kernels. Collect the popped kernels in a bowl.

2. Use the scoop to gather the popped corn kernels. Using the triple-beam balance, weigh out exactly one gram (g) of popped corn kernels.

3. Place the wire gauze on top of the tripod stand.

4. Measure 250 ml of water in the graduated cylinder. Pour the water into the 500-ml beaker. Place the beaker on top of the wire gauze.

5. Insert the thermometer into the beaker containing the 250 ml of water. Wait two minutes. Then note and record the temperature in degrees Celsius (initial temperature) in the Data Collection and Analysis section.

6. Put the gram of popcorn in the porcelain dish; using the spatula or scoop, try to mound it into the shape of a hill. Place the porcelain dish directly under the beaker of water.

(continued)

How Many Calories Are in a Gram of Popcorn? *(continued)*

✋ **Do not do steps 7 and 8 unless an adult is there to supervise!**

7. Put on your lab apron and safety goggles now! Using a lighted match, set the hill of popcorn on fire. Popcorn burns easily, and you can start the hill burning by applying the lit match to the top of the hill. Once the popcorn is burning, remove the match and extinguish it.

8. Be sure that all the popcorn has burned. If not, use another lighted match to ignite any unburned popcorn. Do this as quickly as possible.

9. When all the popcorn has been burned, stir the water gently with the thermometer. Then read and record the temperature in degrees Celsius (final temperature) in the Data Collection and Analysis section.

10. Repeat steps 2 through 9 with fresh water.

📏 DATA COLLECTION AND ANALYSIS

Trial	Initial Temperature	Final Temperature	Final Temperature Minus Initial Temperature	Column 4 Divided by 4 = Number of Kilocalories in One Gram of Popcorn
1				
2				
Average				

The final temperature minus the initial temperature that you recorded in column 4 is equal to the amount of heat gained by 250 ml of water due to the burning of 1 g of popcorn.

Since you heated only ¼ of 1,000 ml, or 250 ml, the rise in temperature for 1,000 ml would be ¼ as much. Thus, you must divide the temperature change by 4 to determine the number of kilocalories in 1 g of popcorn.

(continued)

How Many Calories Are in a Gram of Popcorn? *(continued)*

? CONCLUDING QUESTIONS

1. A serving of popcorn is 1 cupful (6 g). According to your calculations, how many calories are in one serving of popcorn? _____

2. If you don't want to gain weight, why is it wiser to eat air-popped popcorn than to eat popcorn popped in oil? _____

   _____

3. Put your group's data on the chalkboard and compare your results with the data of the other groups in your class.

4. What conditions must be changed in the setup of your equipment to make your results more accurate?

   _____

   _____

   _____

 **Follow-up Activities**

1. Repeat this activity using a different brand of popcorn. How do the results compare?

2. Keep a record of the calories you consume in one day by using charts in textbooks, pamphlets, food labels, and the Internet.

3. Compare the calories in popcorn with the calories in other snack foods.

What Part of Popcorn Is Air?

✔ INSTRUCTIONAL OBJECTIVES

Students will be able to

- record and analyze data.
- draw conclusions based upon data.
- determine the volume of solid material in popcorn kernels.
- establish a ratio.

🌐 NATIONAL SCIENCE STANDARDS ADDRESSED

Students demonstrate an understanding of

- the properties of matter.
- big ideas and unifying concepts, such as cause and effect.

Students demonstrate scientific inquiry and problem-solving skills by

- identifying problems.
- working in teams to collect data.

Students demonstrate competence with the tools of science by

- using scientific equipment.

✂ MATERIALS

- 🤚 Food processor or food chopper and cutting board
- One cup of corn kernels
- 🤚 Hot-air popcorn maker
- Spatula or scoop
- 10-ml graduated cylinder
- 250-ml graduated cylinder
- Bowl to collect the popcorn

🤚 = Safety icon

🖥 INTERNET TIE-INS

http://chemwww.byu.edu/classes/chem/1052/doc/popcorn.html
http://www.point-and-click.com.kids/popcorn.html

❓ QUIZ

1. What is inside a bowl of popcorn besides solid matter?
2. Describe one way to measure the volume of solid material that is in a bowlful of popcorn.

HELPFUL HINTS AND DISCUSSION

Time frame: One to two periods
Structure: In cooperative learning groups
Location: In class or at home

A hot-air popcorn maker is suggested because it is the safest way to make popcorn. **Students should be cautioned not to touch the popcorn maker until it has had a chance to cool down. Handling of the food processor blade or chopping blade must be done under the direct supervision of a teacher or another adult.** Students are advised to cut the pieces of popcorn with the sharpest blade in order to avoid compressing the pieces; compression would change the volume measurement. It would be helpful to go over the mathematical reasoning involved in this activity.

ADAPTATIONS FOR HIGH AND LOW ACHIEVERS

High Achievers: These students should be encouraged to carry out the Follow-up Activities. They should also assist the low achievers with carrying out this activity and collecting and analyzing the data.

Low Achievers: These students should be helped with the mathematical tasks and should be carefully supervised when they are handling the food processor and hot-air popper.

SCORING RUBRIC

Full credit should be given to those students who record the data correctly and who do the mathematics correctly. They also should answer all of the Concluding Questions. Extra credit can be given if any of the Follow-up Activities are completed.

What Part of Popcorn Is Air?

👀 BEFORE YOU BEGIN 👀

What nutritional value is there in a bucket of popcorn? What part of it is air with no nutritional value at all? This activity will give you some food for thought so that you will have a better idea of how to answer these questions. In this activity you will find out what part of a popped popcorn kernel is air.

✂ MATERIALS

- 🖐 Food processor or food chopper and cutting board
- One cup of corn kernels
- 🖐 Hot-air popcorn maker
- Spatula or scoop
- 10-ml graduated cylinder
- 250-ml graduated cylinder
- Bowl to collect the popcorn

🖐 = Safety icon

📦 PROCEDURE

1. Place 25 unpopped kernels in the 10-ml graduated cylinder and measure their volume. Record the volume to the nearest milliliter in the Data Collection and Analysis section.

2. Place 70 to 80 kernels in the hot-air popper and put the collecting bowl under the popcorn chute. Pop the corn. **Avoid touching the popcorn maker until it cools down!**

3. Remove 25 popped kernels from the collecting bowl and put them in the large graduated cylinder. Tap the cylinder with two fingers, as shown in the diagram below. Note and record the volume of the popped kernels in the Data Collection and Analysis section.

4. After you have measured the volume of the popped kernels, remove the 25 popped kernels from the graduated cylinder and transfer them to the food processor or chopping board.

5. **This step must be done under the supervision of your teacher or other responsible adult.** Using the sharpest blade in the food processor, cut the 25 popped kernels into many small pieces. If you **don't** have a food processor, use a sharp food chopper and chopping board.

6. Use the spatula or scoop to put **all** of the small pieces of popcorn into the large graduated cylinder. Gently tap the cylinder with two fingers once or twice while holding the cylinder in the other hand, as shown in the diagram. This tapping will cause the tiny pieces of flake to settle and will eliminate air spaces.

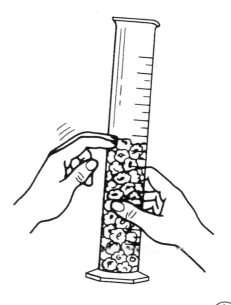

(continued) 🔥

What Part of Popcorn Is Air? *(continued)*

7. Record the volume of the chopped popcorn in the Data Collection and Analysis section. Remove all the pieces of popcorn.

DATA COLLECTION AND ANALYSIS

   (a) The volume of 25 unpopped kernels is _____ ml.

   (b) The volume of 25 uncut popped kernels is _____ ml.

   (c) The volume of 25 chopped popped kernels is _____ ml.

- You now can establish a relationship among the volume of unpopped popcorn kernels, popcorn solid material, and air for 25 pieces of popcorn.

  Suppose the volume of 25 kernels was 5 ml, and the volume of the cut-up popcorn was 10 ml, and the volume of the uncut popcorn was 40 ml. If you divide the volume of the chopped popcorn (10 ml) by the volume of the unpopped kernels (5 ml), you will find that the solid material in the 25 chopped pieces of popcorn increased by a factor of 2 (10 ml/5 ml).

  If you divide the volume of the popped kernels (40 ml) by the volume of the unpopped kernels (5 ml), you will find that popping increases the volume by a factor of 8.

  You also could determine that the ratio of air to solid popcorn material was 4 to 1 (40 to 10). This means that there is four times as much air as popcorn!

- Using *your* figures, how much air would there be in a bucket of popcorn holding 1 liter

  (1,000 ml) of popped corn kernels? _____

(continued)

What Part of Popcorn Is Air? *(continued)*

? CONCLUDING QUESTIONS

1. Why might a food concession at the circus want to use popcorn that has the largest air spaces?

   _____

   _____

2. Put your group's data on the chalkboard and compare your results with the data of the other groups in your class.

3. Imagine you sold 500 buckets, each 1 liter in volume, of popcorn a day at your food stand. How many kernels of popcorn would you have to use each day? (**Hint:** From this activity, you know that 25 kernels will produce a certain volume of popcorn.) How much air is in each bucket? How much solid popcorn material is in each bucket? _____

   _____

4. How are food concessions in theaters and circuses able to keep the popcorn from absorbing moisture and becoming soggy? _____

   _____

5. Why do you think the volume of the cut-up popped popcorn was greater than the volume of the raw kernels?

   _____

   _____

👋 Follow-up Activities 👋

1. Repeat this activity with a different brand of popcorn. How do the results compare?

2. Repeat this activity, but use a microwave oven to pop the kernels instead of a hot-air popper. How do the results compare?

What Nutrients Are in Popcorn Besides Water?

✓ INSTRUCTIONAL OBJECTIVES

Students will be able to

- record and analyze data.
- draw conclusions based upon data.
- determine the presence or absence of several key nutrients in popcorn.

🌐 NATIONAL SCIENCE STANDARDS ADDRESSED

Students demonstrate an understanding of

- health and nutrition.
- big ideas and unifying concepts, such as cause and effect.

Students demonstrate scientific inquiry and problem-solving skills by

- distinguishing causes and effects.
- identifying problems.
- working in teams to collect data.

Students demonstrate competence with the tools of science by

- using scientific equipment.

✂ MATERIALS

- 100 unpopped popcorn kernels
- Mortar and pestle
- (✋)Hot-air popcorn maker
- (✋)Lugol's iodine solution
- Two medicine droppers
- Paper towels for clean up
- Six heat-resistant (Pyrex®) test tubes
- Petri dish
- Piece of unglazed paper from a brown paper bag
- (✋)Matches or gas burner igniter
- Safety goggles
- Laboratory apron
- Scoop
- 50-ml beaker
- 250- to 400-ml beaker
- Test tube holder
- Test tube rack
- Indophenol solution or methylene blue solution
- (✋)Gas or propane burner
- (✋)Biuret solution
- (✋)Benedict's solution

(✋) = Safety icon

HELPFUL HINTS AND DISCUSSION

Time frame: One to two periods
Structure: In cooperative learning groups of two to four students
Location: In class

There are a number of safety issues that must be addressed, including the wearing of safety goggles and a lab coat or apron. The teacher should supervise the heating of Benedict's solution. Prior to carrying out this activity, students should review with the teacher the proper way to light the gas or propane burner and how to hold and direct the test tube being heated.

It is much easier to purchase Lugol's, Benedict's, and Biuret as well as indophenol solutions directly from a scientific supply house than to prepare the solutions yourself. **The iodine in Lugol's solution is toxic if inhaled or ingested. Biuret solution is corrosive to the eyes and other tissues. Obviously, none of the solutions should be ingested since each is toxic to some degree.** Indophenol should be made fresh before using since its shelf life is quite poor. Using an old solution will not yield good results.

In this activity, the students will observe that popcorn does not contain any vitamin C.

ADAPTATIONS FOR HIGH AND LOW ACHIEVERS

High Achievers: These students should be encouraged to carry out the Follow-up Activities. They also should assist the low achievers with this activity, particularly the heating of Benedict's solution and the handling of the Biuret solution.

Low Achievers: These students should be assisted in the carrying out of the nutrition tests, particularly those tests that may be hazardous if not done correctly.

SCORING RUBRIC

Full credit should be given to those students who record the data correctly. They also should answer all of the Concluding Questions. Extra credit can be given if any of the Follow-up Activities are completed.

INTERNET TIE-INS   http://www.point-and-click.com.kids/popcorn.html
http://www.jaring.my/clhs/health.htm

QUIZ

1. State three reasons why popcorn is a healthy snack.
2. State three reasons why eating popcorn is better for your teeth and gums than eating a candy bar.

What Nutrients Are in Popcorn Besides Water?

 **BEFORE YOU BEGIN**

Popcorn is an ideal snack food. As you will find out in this activity, it contains important nutrients. Your dentist would probably approve if you snacked on popcorn because chewing it helps clean your teeth and exercises the gums. It has only a small amount of fat and contains few calories. Finally, popcorn is inexpensive when you compare its cost with that of candy or other snack foods. In this activity, you will determine whether popcorn contains starch, simple sugars, protein, and fat.

MATERIALS

- 100 unpopped popcorn kernels
- Mortar and pestle
- Hot-air popcorn maker
- Lugol's iodine solution
- Two medicine droppers
- Paper towels for clean up
- Six heat-resistant (Pyrex®) test tubes
- Petri dish
- Piece of unglazed paper from a brown paper bag
- Matches or gas burner igniter
- Safety goggles

- Laboratory apron
- Scoop
- 50-ml beaker
- 250- to 400-ml beaker
- Test tube holder
- Test tube rack
- Indophenol solution or methylene blue solution
- Gas or propane burner
- Biuret solution
- Benedict's solution

 = Safety icon

PROCEDURE

1. Using the mortar and pestle, crush 60 unpopped kernels so that the seed coats are broken. It is not necessary to grind them into a powder. Coarse chunks will do nicely. Transfer the chunks to the 50-ml beaker.

2. Pop the remaining 40 kernels in the hot-air popcorn maker. Transfer 25 pieces of popcorn into the large beaker. You can eat the rest.

pestle →

← mortar

   A. Test for Starch—Lugol's solution changes color from red to bluish black if starch is present.

   1) Using the scoop, place some chunks of ground, raw popcorn kernels in one half of the petri dish.

   2) Note the color of the Lugol's solution in the bottle. Record its color in the Data Collection and Analysis section.

(continued)

What Nutrients Are in Popcorn Besides Water? *(continued)*

3) Using the medicine dropper, add several drops of Lugol's solution to the raw kernel chunks.

4) Place five pieces of popped corn in the other half of the petri dish and repeat steps A 1–3.
   In the Data Collection and Analysis section, record the color changes of the Lugol's solution on both the kernel chunks and the popped corn.

B. Test for Simple Sugar—When heated, Benedict's solution turns from blue to green if a trace of a simple sugar is present. A reddish-orange **precipitate** forms if there is more than a trace of a simple sugar.

1) Note the color of the Benedict's solution in the test tube before you heat it. Record its color in the Data Collection and Analysis section.

2) **The heating of the Benedict's solution must be done under your teacher's supervision. Put on your safety goggles and apron now.** Place a small amount of crushed kernels in one test tube, and add enough Benedict's solution to cover them. Following your teacher's instructions, light the gas burner.

3) Using the test tube holder, hold the test tube with the crushed kernels and the Benedict's solution above the flame, and slowly heat until the Benedict's solution boils. Make sure NOT to point the test tube toward anyone, including yourself. Observe the color of the test tube's contents and record it in the Data Collection and Analysis section.

4) Repeat steps B 1–3, but use five pieces of popped corn that you have mashed. Record your observations in the Data Collection and Analysis section.

C. Test for Protein—Cover the popcorn sample with Biuret solution. If protein is present, the solution will turn pink.

1) In the Data Collection and Analysis section, record the color of the Biuret
   solution in the bottle before you use it.

2) **Be sure your safety goggles and apron are on.** Place a small amount of crushed kernels in a clean test tube and add enough Biuret solution to cover them.

3) Observe the color of the test tube's contents and record it in the Data Collection and Analysis section.

4) Repeat steps C 1–3, but use five pieces of popped corn that you have chopped up. Record your observations in the Data Collection and Analysis section.

(continued)

What Nutrients Are in Popcorn Besides Water? *(continued)*

D. Test for Fats—Rub the popcorn sample on a piece of unglazed paper (piece of a brown paper bag). Hold the paper up to the light. If fat is present, you will see a **translucent** spot where you rubbed the popcorn.

1) Wash and dry your hands thoroughly. Why is it necessary to do this?

2) Take a few chunks of unpopped kernels and rub them firmly on a piece of unglazed paper. Hold the paper up to the light and look for a translucent spot where you rubbed the corn. Record your observations in the Data Collection and Analysis section.

3) Repeat step D 2 using one or two pieces of popped corn. Record your observations in the Data Collection and Analysis section.

E. Test for Vitamin C—Indophenol solution will turn from blue to colorless in the presence of vitamin C. The greater the amount of vitamin C present, the quicker the indophenol solution will lose its color. Ignore any pink color that may form when testing with indophenol.

1) In the Data Collection and Analysis section, write the original color of the indophenol solution.

2) Put 15 drops of indophenol in a clean test tube. Add the remainder of the corn kernel chunks to the test tube. Shake the tube to mix the ingredients. In the Data Collection and Analysis section, describe the color of the solution.

3) Repeat step E 2, but use pieces of popped corn instead of the kernel chunks. In the Data Collection and Analysis section, describe the color of the solution.

DATA COLLECTION AND ANALYSIS

- Color of Lugol's solution in the bottle is _____.
- Color of Lugol's on raw kernel chunks is _____.
- Color of Lugol's on popped corn is _____.
- Color of Benedict's solution in the test tube before heating is _____.
- Color of Benedict's solution in the test tube with crushed kernels after heating is

  _____.

- Color of Benedict's solution in the test tube with popped corn after heating is _____.
- Color of Biuret solution in the bottle is _____.
- Color of Biuret solution with raw kernel chunks is _____.
- Color of Biuret solution with popped corn is _____.
- Appearance of unglazed paper after being rubbed with unpopped kernels is _____.
- Appearance of unglazed paper after being rubbed with popcorn is _____.
- Color of the original indophenol solution is _____.
- Color of the indophenol solution containing raw kernel chunks is _____.
- Color of the indophenol solution containing pieces of popped corn is _____.

(continued)

What Nutrients Are in Popcorn Besides Water?

? CONCLUDING QUESTIONS

1. What nutrients did you find in the popcorn? What is the evidence for your answer? _____

   _____

   _____

   _____

2. Why were you asked to test pieces of kernels and also pieces of popcorn in each case? _____

   _____

   _____

   _____

3. Why were you told to wash and dry your hands thoroughly before testing for fats? _____

   _____

   _____

   _____

👆 Follow-up Activities 👆

1. Repeat this activity using popcorn popped with melted butter. How do the results compare?

2. Test corn kernels and popcorn for disaccharides by using Barfoed's test. Report your results to the class.

3. Test unpopped kernels and popcorn for ketose sugars by using Selivanoff's test. Report your results to the class.

4. Add a few pieces of kernels and then popped corn to a few granules of Sudan IV to test for the presence of fats. How do your results with Sudan IV compare with those using unglazed paper?

Where Is the Fat?

✓ INSTRUCTIONAL OBJECTIVES

Students will be able to

- record and analyze data.
- analyze mathematical relationships and concepts.
- draw conclusions based upon data.

🌐 NATIONAL SCIENCE STANDARDS ADDRESSED

Students demonstrate an understanding of

- big ideas and unifying concepts, such as cause and effect.
- health and nutrition.

Students demonstrate scientific inquiry and problem-solving skills by

- distinguishing causes and effects.
- working in teams to collect and share information.
- identifying the outcomes of an investigation.

Students demonstrate effective scientific communication by

- explaining scientific concepts to others.

✂ MATERIALS

- Four test tubes
- Fat-free (skim) milk
- 1% milk
- 2% milk
- Whole milk
- Sudan IV crystals
- Water
- Medicine dropper
- Microscope
- Four plastic or glass microscope slides
- Four plastic or glass coverslips
- Red crayon
- Lens paper
- Chemical scoop
- Test tube rack

HELPFUL HINTS AND DISCUSSION

Time frame: One to two periods
Structure: In cooperative learning groups
Location: In class

Review how to use the microscope and prepare a wet mount. You may wish to substitute a hemacytometer for slides in order to make the task of counting the stained fat droplets easier. If you decide to use the hemacytometer, your students will need instructions for its use. A brief review of ratios may be necessary.

ADAPTATIONS FOR HIGH AND LOW ACHIEVERS

High Achievers: These students should be encouraged to carry out the Follow-up Activities.
Low Achievers: These students should work with the high achievers and have their counts of stained fat droplets checked.

SCORING RUBRIC

Full credit should be given to those students who accurately record observations and who provide correct answers in full sentences to the questions. Extra credit can be given if any of the Follow-up Activities are completed.

💻 INTERNET TIE-INS

http://www.goaskalice.columbia.edu/1036.html
http://www.itlnet.net/users/k21/DIET/math.html
http://www.med.virginia.edu/docs/heart/docs/education/healthy.html

❓ QUIZ

1. Why has the name of skim milk been changed to fat-free milk?
2. Describe an experiment to compare the relative amounts of fat in whole milk, 2% milk, 1% milk, and fat-free (skim) milk.

Where Is the Fat?

👋 BEFORE YOU BEGIN 👋

Many people think of fat as being bad for you. The truth is that fats are essential to good health. Your body stores energy in fat. Your body fat also acts as an insulator against the cold and as a shock absorber, preventing serious injury if you should fall or be bumped. In addition, the cells in your body contain fat in their cell membranes. In this activity, you will test several kinds of milk for the presence of fat. You will also attempt to determine relative amounts of fat in several types of milk, including whole milk, 2% milk, 1% milk, and fat-free (skim) milk.

MATERIALS

- Four test tubes
- Fat-free (skim) milk
- 1% milk
- 2% milk
- Whole milk
- Sudan IV crystals
- Water
- Medicine dropper

- Microscope
- Four plastic or glass microscope slides
- Four plastic or glass coverslips
- Red crayon
- Lens paper
- Chemical scoop
- Test tube rack

PROCEDURE

1. Fill a test tube half full of water. Using a chemical scoop, add five or six crystals of Sudan IV. Shake the test tube to dissolve the crystals.

2. Add 40 drops of whole milk, using a clean medicine dropper. Shake the test tube and its contents well.

3. Clean both the microscope slide and coverslip with lens paper. Place a drop of the liquid you prepared in steps 1 and 2 onto a microscope slide.

4. Cover the liquid with the coverslip.

5. Examine the drop under the low-power objective of the microscope. See if the Sudan IV in your mixture has turned red. If this reaction did take place, then you will find red-stained little round fat droplets. Count the number of red-stained fat droplets that you see under low power. Record that number in the space provided in the Data Collection and Analysis section. Draw and color what you see in the appropriate circle in the Data Collection and Analysis section.

6. Repeat steps 1 through 5, substituting fat-free (skim) milk for the whole milk.

7. Repeat steps 1 through 5, substituting 1% milk for the whole milk.

8. Repeat steps 1 through 5, substituting 2% milk for the whole milk.

(continued)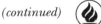

Where Is the Fat? *(continued)*

 DATA COLLECTION AND ANALYSIS

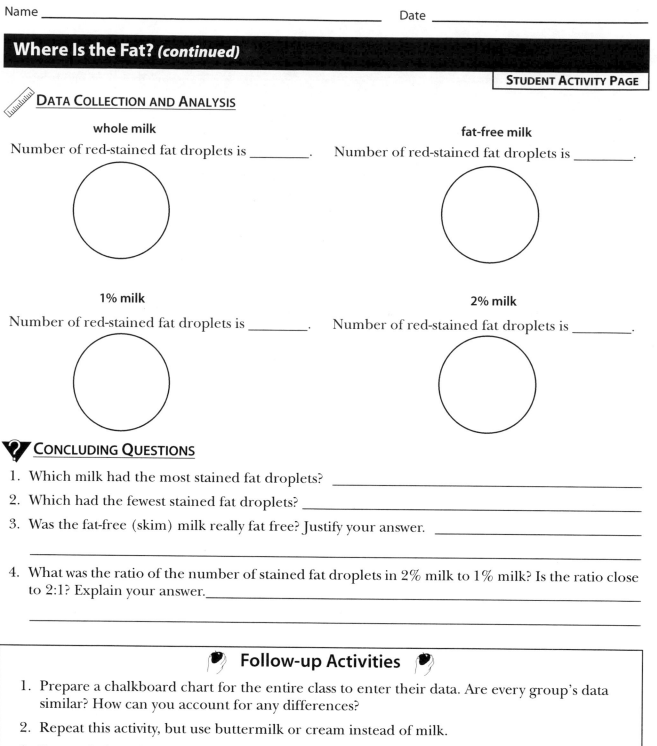

whole milk

Number of red-stained fat droplets is _____.

fat-free milk

Number of red-stained fat droplets is _____.

1% milk

Number of red-stained fat droplets is _____.

2% milk

Number of red-stained fat droplets is _____.

CONCLUDING QUESTIONS

1. Which milk had the most stained fat droplets? _____

2. Which had the fewest stained fat droplets? _____

3. Was the fat-free (skim) milk really fat free? Justify your answer. _____

_____

4. What was the ratio of the number of stained fat droplets in 2% milk to 1% milk? Is the ratio close to 2:1? Explain your answer. _____

_____

👆 Follow-up Activities 👆

1. Prepare a chalkboard chart for the entire class to enter their data. Are every group's data similar? How can you account for any differences?

2. Repeat this activity, but use buttermilk or cream instead of milk.

3. Research the role of cholesterol in the formation of useful body chemicals called **steroids** and in the formation of plaque inside arteries. Report your findings to the class.

Which Has the Most Vitamin C?

✔ INSTRUCTIONAL OBJECTIVES

Students will be able to

- record and analyze data.
- draw conclusions based upon data.
- determine the relative strength of several vitamin C solutions.

🌐 NATIONAL SCIENCE STANDARDS ADDRESSED

Students demonstrate an understanding of

- health and nutrition.
- big ideas and unifying concepts, such as cause and effect.

Students demonstrate scientific inquiry and problem-solving skills by

- distinguishing causes and effects.
- identifying problems.
- carrying out a controlled experiment.
- identifying variables in an experiment.
- working individually to collect data.

Students demonstrate competence with the tools of science by

- using scientific equipment.

✂ MATERIALS

- Freshly squeezed lemon juice
- Lemon juice from concentrate
- Frozen lemonade
- Freshly made indophenol solution
- Four medicine droppers
- Four test tubes
- Test tube rack
- Vitamin C tablet (250 mg) and water
- Knife
- Stirring rod
- 25-ml graduated cylinder

💻 INTERNET TIE-INS

http://www.dole5aday.com
http://www.immortality.org

QUIZ

1. Describe the test for vitamin C.

HELPFUL HINTS AND DISCUSSION

Time frame: One period
Structure: Individually
Location: In class

Prepare a 0.1% solution of indophenol by dissolving 1 g of 2,6-dichloroindophenol, sodium salt in 1 L of water. (Indophenol solutions have a poor shelf life, so make up a fresh solution on the day you plan to have your students do this activity.) Cut a vitamin C tablet in half. Discard one half. Dissolve the other half tablet in 100 ml of water. Stir if the half tablet doesn't dissolve. This solution will be your stock vitamin C solution. If you find that one drop of the ascorbic acid solution bleaches the indophenol solution, dilute it further by adding another 100 ml of water.

ADAPTATIONS FOR HIGH AND LOW ACHIEVERS

High Achievers: These students should be encouraged to carry out the Follow-up Activities. They also should assist the low achievers with this activity.

Low Achievers: These students should be assisted in the testing of the solutions and in understanding the variables in this experiment.

SCORING RUBRIC

Full credit should be given to those students who record the data correctly. They also should answer all of the Concluding Questions. Extra credit can be given if any of the Follow-up Activities are completed.

Name _____   Date _____

Which Has the Most Vitamin C?

👆 BEFORE YOU BEGIN 👆

Of all the vitamins, vitamin C is perhaps the best known. It is known to chemists as **ascorbic acid**. It has been linked to preventing colds and cancer.

In this activity, you will test freshly squeezed lemon juice, lemon juice from concentrate, and frozen lemonade for their vitamin C content. You will use a chemical known as **indophenol** as an indicator. It normally is a bluish liquid, but it turns colorless in the presence of vitamin C. You can get a close approximation of the amount of vitamin C that is present when using indophenol because the higher the concentration of vitamin C, the fewer the drops needed to bleach the indophenol. For example, two drops of solution X bleaches an indophenol solution, but it takes six drops of solution Y to bleach the same strength indophenol solution. Therefore, solution X would contain more vitamin C than solution Y would.

✂ MATERIALS

- Freshly squeezed lemon juice
- Lemon juice from concentrate
- Frozen lemonade
- Freshly made indophenol solution
- Four medicine droppers
- Four test tubes

- Test tube rack
- Vitamin C tablet (250 mg) and water
- 25-ml graduated cylinder
- Knife
- Stirring rod
- 25-ml graduated cylinder

📦 PROCEDURE

1. Using the graduated cylinder, add 10 ml of the indophenol solution to a test tube. In the Data Collection and Analysis section, describe the color of the solution.

2. With a medicine dropper, add one drop of the vitamin C solution to the test tube containing the 10 ml of indophenol solution. Check the color. Then, continue to add additional drops of vitamin C solution, one drop at a time, making sure to shake the test tube after each drop has been added, until the indophenol becomes colorless. You may notice that during the process the indophenol first turns from blue to pink. This is an intermediate step and does not mean that the reaction is complete.

3. In the Data Collection and Analysis section, record the number of drops that were necessary to completely bleach the indophenol in step 2.

4. Repeat steps 1, 2, and 3, but use freshly squeezed lemon juice.

5. Repeat steps 1, 2, and 3, but use lemon juice from concentrate.

6. Repeat steps 1, 2, and 3, but use the frozen lemonade that has been thawed.

(continued) 🔥

Which Has the Most Vitamin C? *(continued)*

DATA COLLECTION AND ANALYSIS

1. Color of the indophenol solution is _____.

2. Number of drops of the vitamin C solution necessary to completely bleach the indophenol is _____.

3. Number of drops of freshly squeezed lemon juice necessary to bleach the indophenol is _____.

4. Number of drops of lemon juice from concentrate necessary to bleach the indophenol is _____.

5. Number of drops of thawed lemonade necessary to bleach the indophenol is _____.

CONCLUDING QUESTIONS

1. Which solution took the fewest drops to bleach the indophenol solution? _____

   _____

2. Which solution required the most drops to bleach the indophenol solution? _____

   _____

3. Rank the solutions in terms of the amount of vitamin C in each, starting with the solution that had the most vitamin C. _____

   _____

   _____

👆 Follow-up Activities 👆

1. Repeat this activity, but use juice freshly squeezed from an apple, frozen apple juice, and apple juice from a bottle.

2. Design a method for determining the strength of a vitamin C solution. Show your plan to your teacher; then test it.

3. Repeat this activity comparing freshly squeezed lemon juice with lemon juice that has been left uncovered outside the refrigerator for a day.

No Sweat, No Water Loss

☑ INSTRUCTIONAL OBJECTIVES

Students will be able to

- record and analyze data.
- draw conclusions based upon data.
- explain the importance of sweating and temperature regulation.
- determine the percentage of body weight lost during an exercise period.

🌐 NATIONAL SCIENCE STANDARDS ADDRESSED

Students demonstrate an understanding of

- response to stimuli.
- function in living systems.
- regulation and behavior.
- big ideas and unifying concepts, such as cause and effect.

Students demonstrate scientific inquiry and problem-solving skills by

- distinguishing causes and effects.
- identifying problems.
- working individually to collect data.

Students demonstrate competence with the tools of science by

- using scientific equipment.

✂ MATERIALS

- Bathroom scale
- Towel
- Three 8-oz. glasses of water

HELPFUL HINTS AND DISCUSSION

Time frame: One period
Structure: Individually
Location: At home

This activity focuses on the removal of excess heat through the evaporation of sweat formed during exercise. Those who engage in this activity will measure their weight before and after exercising strenuously for 15 minutes. It is important to drink the three glasses of water prior to exercising. Students should be cautioned not to drink during the exercise period. Finally, urge students to replace the water lost during exercise by drinking plain water.

✋ **Students should be aware of any physical conditions that would make strenuous activity dangerous for them. Students should have parental consent before beginning this activity.**

ADAPTATIONS FOR HIGH AND LOW ACHIEVERS

High Achievers: These students should be encouraged to carry out the Follow-up Activities and answer all items in the Concluding Questions.

Low Achievers: These students should be helped in using the formula for the percentage of body weight lost.

SCORING RUBRIC

Full credit should be given to those students who record observations and who provide correct answers in full sentences to the questions. Extra credit can be given if any of the Follow-up Activities are completed.

 INTERNET TIE-INS   http://www.clark.net/pub/pribut/humidtxt.html
http://library.advanced.org/10348/

❓ QUIZ   1. When the body temperature rises above normal, the skin becomes reddened owing to expansion of the small blood vessels in the skin. Explain why this action will promote cooling.
2. Why is **dehydration** a serious medical condition?

44

No Sweat, No Water Loss

 BEFORE YOU BEGIN

As you already know, water is necessary for survival. The majority of your body weight is water, and if you were to lose 20 percent of that water, you would probably die!

When you perform any physical activity—whether walking, eating, or running—only 25 percent of energy released by the body is mechanical energy. The other 75 percent is heat. That extra heat must be removed to avoid dangerously increasing the body's temperature by more than three degrees Celsius. To cool your body, sweat—which is mainly water and a small amount of salt—evaporates from your skin. This process is called **perspiration**.

You perspire all the time, even in cold weather. The main job of perspiration is to remove heat from the skin. When moisture on the skin evaporates, heat energy is required for that process to occur. The effect is a cooling of the skin. You can lose up to two liters of water in the form of sweat when running or playing basketball. A person who runs in a 20-mile marathon race may lose more than two kilograms of water during the race.

In this activity, you are going to measure the amount of liquid that you lose during 15 minutes of strenuous exercise, such as running around your block or doing push-ups.

It is most important that you follow the directions for drinking water (water is better than juice or soda) before and after exercising to prevent *dehydration* **(drying out).**

MATERIALS

- Bathroom scale
- Towel
- Three 8-oz. glasses of water

PROCEDURE

NOTE: If you have any physical disabilities that prevent you from engaging in strenuous exercise, or if you feel that you do not have the stamina to complete this activity, do not attempt it. Make sure that you get your parent's permission before doing this activity.

1. Two hours before exercising, drink two 8-oz. glasses of water, even if you are not thirsty. One-half hour before exercising, drink the other glass of water. **This is important!**

2. Weigh yourself on your bathroom scale *without* any clothes on before you exercise. Record your weight to the nearest pound in the Data Collection and Analysis section.

3. Dress. Wear light, porous, loose clothing. Don't wear rubberized clothing designed to increase sweating. All such clothing does is to prevent the sweat from evaporating.

4. Engage in some vigorous physical activity (running, doing push-ups, etc.) for 15 minutes. **Do this step under adult supervision.**

(continued)

No Sweat, No Water Loss (continued)

5. Return to your bathroom and remove your clothing. Use the towel to thoroughly remove any remaining sweat.

6. Step on the scale. Observe what you weigh now, and record that amount in the Data Collection and Analysis section.

7. Drink water to replace the lost fluid, one glass for every half pound. If you still feel thirsty, drink more water.

DATA COLLECTION AND ANALYSIS

1. Weight before exercising is _____ pounds.

2. Weight after exercising is _____ pounds.

3. Water lost during exercise is _____ pounds.

4. What percentage of your body weight did you lose by exercising?

$$\% = \frac{\text{Water lost (pounds)}}{\text{Body weight (pounds) before exercising}} \times 100$$

CONCLUDING QUESTIONS

1. What are the dangers in NOT replacing water that is lost by exercising?

_____

_____

2. Why are fans useful for cooling the body? _____

_____

_____

3. Name several body functions that depend upon water. _____

_____

_____

👆 Follow-up Activities 👆

1. Research the role of the brain in regulating body temperature.

2. Repeat this activity on a very cool, dry day and also on a very hot, humid day. How do your results compare with those obtained during the initial activity?

3. Research how antiperspirants work.

Milk, Hot Dogs, and Nutritional Math

✓ INSTRUCTIONAL OBJECTIVES

Students will be able to

- record and analyze data.
- explain mathematical relationships and concepts.
- draw conclusions based upon data.
- determine their approximate intake of calcium in a day.
- explain the difference between percent of fat calories and percent of fat by weight in a serving size.

🌐 NATIONAL SCIENCE STANDARDS ADDRESSED

Students demonstrate an understanding of

- big ideas and unifying concepts, such as cause and effect.
- health and nutrition.

Students demonstrate scientific inquiry and problem-solving skills by

- distinguishing causes and effects.
- identifying the outcomes of an investigation.
- working individually or in teams to collect and share information.

Students demonstrate effective scientific communication by

- explaining scientific concepts to others.

Students demonstrate competence with the tools and technologies of science by

- acquiring information from multiple sources.

✂ MATERIALS

- 1% milk label
- 2% milk label
- Whole-milk label
- Pencil or pen
- Beef hot dog label
- Turkey hot dog label

💻 INTERNET TIE-INS

http://www.bc-dairy-foundation.org/bcdf/calcium5.gif
http://www.whymilk.com/about/nutrient/index.html
http://www.enc.org/reform/journals

❓ QUIZ

1. How can food labels be used to determine the amount of fat by weight in a serving?
2. Name three foods that are good sources of calcium.

HELPFUL HINTS AND DISCUSSION

Time frame: One to two periods
Structure: In cooperative learning groups or individually
Location: In class

Review the various mathematical formulas used in this activity. Discuss the difference between the percent of fat calories and the percent of fat by weight in a serving size. Be sure your students know the meaning of the term **serving size**.

ADAPTATIONS FOR HIGH AND LOW ACHIEVERS

High Achievers: These students should be encouraged to carry out the Follow-up Activities and assist the low achievers with their calculations.

Low Achievers: These students should work with the high achievers in deriving the percentages of fat per serving.

SCORING RUBRIC

Full credit should be given to those students who accurately record observations and who provide correct answers in full sentences to the questions. Extra credit can be given if any of the Follow-up Activities are completed.

Milk, Hot Dogs, and Nutritional Math

☞ BEFORE YOU BEGIN ☞

In this activity, you will convert grams of fat to calories, and you will compute the percentage of fat in a serving of milk and hot dogs. You will also calculate the percentage of your calcium intake from milk and other foods. Calcium is essential for bones to grow normally and strong. A recent survey revealed that 85% of teenage girls and 60% of teenage boys weren't getting enough calcium on a daily basis.

✂ MATERIALS

- 1% milk label
- 2% milk label
- Whole-milk label

- Pencil or pen
- Beef hot dog label
- Turkey hot dog label

📦 PROCEDURE

1. Look at the whole milk label, and take note of the fact that the serving size is one cup. For this activity, you will be concerned only with *the total number of calories* and *the number of grams of fat* in one serving. The label states that there are 150 calories and 8 grams of fat in a one-cup (240 ml) serving of milk. Each gram of fat accounts for only 9 of these calories. So, there will be 72 (8 × 9) calories from fat in a cup of milk.

2. To work out the percentage of fat calories, you must divide the number of fat calories by the total number of calories in the one-cup serving of milk and multiply by 100.

   In this case,

   $$\frac{72 \text{ total calories from fat}}{150 \text{ total calories}} \times 100 = 48\%$$

   Therefore, 48 percent of the calories in a glass of whole milk come from fat.

3. Whole milk is 3.3 percent fat. You can prove this by dividing the number of grams of fat in a serving by the weight (grams) in a serving. Assume that 1 ml of milk weighs 1 g. The formula you will use is

   $$\frac{\text{Grams of fat per serving of whole milk}}{\text{Total grams per serving of whole milk}} \times 100 = \frac{800}{2400} = 3.3\%$$

   As you work with the other milk labels, use this formula to check that 1% milk is really 1%. Do the same for 2% milk.

4. Repeat Steps 1, 2, and 3, but use the 2% milk label. Record your calculations in the Data Collection and Analysis section.

5. Repeat Steps 1, 2, and 3, but use the 1% milk label. Record your calculations in the Data Collection and Analysis section.

(continued)

Milk, Hot Dogs, and Nutritional Math *(continued)*

6. Now look at your hot dog labels. First, note that the serving size of each type is one hot dog. However, one turkey hot dog (a serving size) weighs 45 g while one beef hot dog (a serving size) may weigh 56 g. Use the hot dog labels to enter the necessary information in the Data Collection and Analysis section on the next page. Use these figures to determine the percentage of calories from fat and the percentage of fat per serving for each type of hot dog.

7. Turn to page 50, which lists foods that are high in calcium. This list will guide you as you estimate your calcium intake. At your age, you need approximately 1,200 milligrams of calcium each day. You can use the number of servings of calcium-rich foods that you ate yesterday, or you can start with today's food intake in order to calculate your total intake of calcium.

8. Circle the food you ate, check the normal serving size, and in the space provided, write in the number of normal servings you consumed. Then, multiply this number by the number of milligrams per serving. Finally, total up your intake for one day. Write the total in the Data Collection and Analysis section.

DATA COLLECTION AND ANALYSIS

2% milk

- Serving size = _____.
- Grams of fat per serving = _____.
- Calories from fat (grams of fat × 9) = _____.
- Total calories per serving = _____.
- Percentage of calories from fat = _____.
- Percentage of fat by weight per serving = _____.

1% milk

- Serving size = _____.
- Grams of fat per serving = _____.
- Calories from fat (grams of fat × 9) = _____.
- Total calories per serving = _____.
- Percentage of calories from fat = _____.
- Percentage of fat by weight per serving = _____.

(continued)

Milk, Hot Dogs, and Nutritional Math *(continued)*

Hot dogs
type (beef, turkey, etc.) _____

- Serving size = _____.
- Grams of fat per serving = _____.
- Calories from fat (grams of fat × 9) = _____.
- Total calories per serving = _____.
- Percentage of calories from fat = _____.
- Percentage of fat by weight per serving = _____.

type (beef, turkey, etc.) _____

- Serving size = _____.
- Grams of fat per serving = _____.
- Calories from fat (grams of fat × 9) = _____.
- Total calories per serving = _____.
- Percentage of calories from fat = _____.
- Percentage of fat by weight per serving = _____.

Calcium-Rich Foods

Food	Serving Size	Number of Servings Eaten	Mg of Calcium per Serving	Total Mg of Calcium Eaten
Milkshake	10 oz.		350	
Hard cheeses: cheddar (edam)	1" × 1" × 3"		350	
Plain yogurt	1 cup		350	
Liquid milk	1 cup		300	
Powdered milk	$\frac{1}{3}$ cup		300	
Yogurt with fruit	1 cup		300	
Processed cheese	2 slices		250	
Soft cheeses (feta)	1" × 1" × 3"		250	
Cheese pizza	1 slice		150	
Pudding	$\frac{1}{2}$ cup		150	
Frozen yogurt	$\frac{1}{2}$ cup		150	
Cottage cheese	$\frac{1}{2}$ cup		75	
Ice cream	$\frac{1}{2}$ cup		75	

Number of milligrams of calcium consumed in one day = _____.

(continued)

Milk, Hot Dogs, and Nutritional Math *(continued)*

▼ CONCLUDING QUESTIONS

1. Which food contained the largest number of calories from fat per serving size? _____

   _____

2. Which food had the fewest fat calories per serving? _____

   _____

3. Which food had the highest percentage of fat by weight for a serving? _____

   _____

4. Based upon your calculations, do you feel you consume too few or too many milligrams of calcium each day? _____

   _____

👆 Follow-up Activities 👆

1. Examine the food labels of prepared foods—such as frozen dinners and chicken pot pies— and snack foods—like potato chips and pretzels. Find the percentage of fat calories and the percentage of fat by weight.

2. Research other uses of calcium by the body in addition to building strong bones. Report your findings to the class.

3. Research to find out if vegetables and fruits are good calcium sources. Share your information with your classmates.

4. Compare the percentages of fat found in regular and "light" products of the same kind. For example, look at regular and low-fat ice cream.

How Fast Do You React?

✔ INSTRUCTIONAL OBJECTIVES

Students will be able to

- record and analyze data.
- analyze mathematical relationships and concepts.
- draw conclusions based upon data.
- compare the rates of response to visual and to auditory stimuli.

🌐 NATIONAL SCIENCE STANDARDS ADDRESSED

Students demonstrate an understanding of

- big ideas and unifying concepts, such as cause and effect.
- regulation and behavior.
- response to environmental stimuli.

Students demonstrate scientific inquiry and problem-solving skills by

- distinguishing causes and effects.
- working in teams to collect and share information.
- identifying the outcomes of an investigation.

Students demonstrate effective scientific communication by

- explaining scientific concepts to others.

✂ MATERIALS

- Meterstick
- Household glue
- Pen or pencil
- Paper blindfold with two strings attached
- Desk and chair
- Scissors

💻 INTERNET TIE-INS

http://www.autobahn.org/~steevm/Webnotes/Bio1A/bio/aw6d2.3.html
http://uwa.edu.au

❓ QUIZ

1. Why are quick reflexes important for doing athletic activities successfully?
2. List four occupations that require quick reflexes.

HELPFUL HINTS AND DISCUSSION

Time frame: One period
Structure: In cooperative learning groups of two students
Location: In class

Review with students how to make and use the timing device. Explain to the students the reason that the 0.01 second marks on the timing tape are continually increasing in length. Also point out the need for honesty in carrying out this activity; emphasize that this is a scientific inquiry, not a competition. Define the term **stimulus**.

ADAPTATIONS FOR HIGH AND LOW ACHIEVERS

High Achievers: These students should be encouraged to carry out the Follow-up Activities.

Low Achievers: These students should work with the high achievers and should be given several practice drops for both the sight and sound portions of the activity.

SCORING RUBRIC

Full credit should be given to those students who accurately record observations and who provide correct answers in full sentences to the questions. Extra credit can be given if any of the Follow-up Activities are completed.

How Fast Do You React?

✋ BEFORE YOU BEGIN ✋

Professional athletic stars have very quick reflexes that often are the key to their success and stardom. This activity will determine how fast you are able to catch a falling rod. You will determine if sight or sound as a **stimulus** will cause you to react faster.

✂ MATERIALS

- Meterstick
- Household glue
- Desk and chair
- Pen or pencil
- Paper blindfold with two strings attached
- Scissors

PROCEDURE

1. You will need to prepare a timing device by using the diagram on page 55. A meterstick is ideal for this purpose. Cut out the scales in the left column. Paste the first scale—the one with the words, "PLACE THUMB HERE"—at the bottom of the blank side of the meterstick. Paste the second strip—the one that contains .21 to .29—just above the .20 line. You should now have one long strip beginning with "PLACE THUMB HERE" and ending with .29. Each division represents one hundredth of a second.

2. One member of your group will be the experimenter, and the other member will be the test subject. After three trials, switch roles.

3. The test subject should sit at a desk sideways, with his or her forearm (either right or left) resting on the desk top and extended over the edge of the desk. The timing stick will drop between the test subject's forefinger and thumb. The experimenter holds the timing stick at the top, with the "PLACE THUMB HERE" position level with the subject's thumb and forefinger. The rest of the timing stick is positioned above the table.

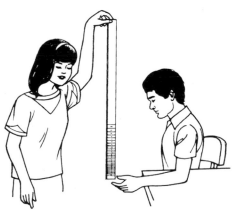

4. The subject should look at the fingers of the experimenter and be ready to catch the falling timing stick as quickly as possible. When the subject is ready, the experimenter should drop the timing stick. When it starts to fall, the subject should try to catch it as soon as possible with his or her thumb and forefinger.

5. When the subject grabs the timing stick, the experimenter should read off the time in hundredths of a second directly from the timing device. For example, if the subject's thumb is between two divisions on the timing stick, such as .21 and .22, read that as 0.215 seconds.

6. Record your results in the table for Visual Stimulus in the Data Collection and Analysis section. Repeat twice more, and record these results as well. Then calculate and record the average time.

(continued) 🔥

How Fast Do You React? *(continued)*

7. Blindfold the subject. Then repeat steps 2 through 5. The experimenter should loudly say "Go" when releasing the timing stick. Record your results in the table for Sound Stimulus in the Data Collection and Analysis section. Repeat twice more, and record these results. Then calculate and record the average time.

8. Switch roles. Repeat steps 2 through 6.

9. On the chalkboard, prepare two large charts similar to those in the Data Collection and Analysis section. The charts should be large enough to hold the data for the entire class.

DATA COLLECTION AND ANALYSIS

Visual Stimulus (Eyes Open)

Test Subject (Name)	Time—Trial 1	Time—Trial 2	Time—Trial 3	Average Time

Sound Stimulus (Eyes Blindfolded)

Test Subject (Name)	Time—Trial 1	Time—Trial 2	Time—Trial 3	Average Time

(continued)

How Fast Do You React? *(continued)*

Column 1
.20
.19
.18
.17
.16
.15
.14
.13
.12
.11
.10
.09
.08
.07
.06
.05
0
place thumb HERE

Column 2
.29
.28
.27
.26
.25
.24
.23
.22
.21

How Fast Do You React? *(continued)*

CONCLUDING QUESTIONS

1. According to your data, which stimulus will produce the faster response: sight or sound?

   _____

2. According to the data of the entire class, which stimulus produces the faster response?

   _____

3. How do your data compare with the class average? _____

   _____

4. After examining the data of the entire class, whose reflexes are faster: boys' or girls'?

   _____

Follow-up Activities

1. Using only vision, carry out the same experiment with your family, friends, and neighbors to determine which age group has the fastest and the slowest reflexes. Prepare a chart with the following age groups: 20 to 40 years old, 40 to 60 years old, over 61 years old. Before testing, predict which group you believe will be the fastest and which age group the slowest. How accurate were your predictions?

2. Research the role that reflexes play in survival. Report your results to the class.

(continued)

A Matter of Taste (Component 1: Taste Buds)

✔ INSTRUCTIONAL OBJECTIVES

Students will be able to

- record and analyze data.
- conduct a controlled experiment.
- draw conclusions based upon data.

🌐 NATIONAL SCIENCE STANDARDS ADDRESSED

Students demonstrate an understanding of

- response to environmental stimuli.
- senses and behavior.
- big ideas and unifying concepts, such as cause and effect.

Students demonstrate scientific inquiry and problem-solving skills by

- working in teams to collect and share information.

Students demonstrate effective scientific communication by

- representing data in multiple ways.

 MATERIALS

For each group:

- Three small cups
- Cotton swabs
- Tap water or bottled water
- Three pairs of latex or rubber gloves
- 12 copies of the tongue map (on page 60)
- Pen or pencil
- Dilute salt solution
- Dilute sugar solution
- Dilute vinegar solution
- Dilute white horseradish solution
- 12 test tubes
- Test tube rack

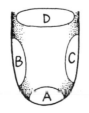

HELPFUL HINTS AND DISCUSSION

Time frame: One period
Structure: In cooperative learning groups of three students each
Location: In class

✋ Swabs are NOT to be dipped in the test solutions in the stock bottle after having been swabbed on a subject's tongue. Each subject should be given a clean swab for each test.

Use a new test tube for each subject and each test. The teacher should prepare stock solutions for the students to use by dissolving 10 g of salt in 500 ml of distilled water, 10 g of sugar in 500 ml of distilled water, 10 ml of vinegar in 500 ml of distilled water, and 10 grams of white horseradish (don't use the red!) in 500 ml of distilled water. It is important to rinse the mouth before and after the mapping procedures. People differ in the number of their taste buds. Those people with a high taste-bud density are more sensitive tasters.

ADAPTATIONS FOR HIGH AND LOW ACHIEVERS

High Achievers: These students should be encouraged to carry out the Follow-up Activities.

Low Achievers: These students may require instructions and practice to achieve the proper technique for swabbing. Use a wall chart of the tongue to illustrate the areas of the tongue to be swabbed. These students should be required to work in cooperative learning groups composed of a mix of high and low achievers. Another possibility is for them to carry out this activity with the help of an educational aide.

SCORING RUBRIC

Full credit should be given to those students who record observations and who provide correct answers in full sentences to all the questions. Extra credit can be given if any of the Follow-up Activities are completed.

 **INTERNET TIE-INS**   http://madsci.wustl.edu
                                 http://www.wfubmc.edu/nba/faculty/miller/miller.html
                                 http://www.kidshealth.org/kid/somebody

QUIZ   1. Explain why the tongue is an important organ in selecting foods.
             2. Which areas of the tongue are sensitive to sugary foods?

A Matter of Taste (Component 1: Taste Buds)

👆 BEFORE YOU BEGIN 👆

When food enters the mouth, it mixes with saliva. This mixture activates the taste buds in the tongue, setting off a chemical reaction that we call "taste." These taste buds can be found on the tongue in large numbers. Taste buds are also found scattered on the cheeks, on the roof of the mouth, and in the throat. To locate your taste buds, stick your tongue out in front of a mirror and look for many little white bumps called **papillae**. At the bottom of many of the papillae, the taste buds will be found. Taste buds can identify four different tastes: **sweet, sour, salty**, and **bitter** in liquids and moist food.

In this activity, you will prepare a map of the areas of the tongue where the different taste buds are located.

 MATERIALS

For each group:

- Three small cups
- Cotton swabs
- Tap water or bottled water
- Three pairs of latex or rubber gloves
- 12 copies of the tongue map
- Pen or pencil

- Dilute salt solution
- Dilute sugar solution
- Dilute vinegar solution
- Dilute white horseradish solution
- 12 test tubes
- Test tube rack

PROCEDURE

1. Work in teams of three students. You will take turns as the experimenter, the recorder, and the subject as you go through each repetition of the experiment. For each new subject, change the order in which the solutions are tested. **The order should NOT be known by the subject**.

2. The person who is acting as the experimenter should place four test tubes in the test tube rack. The tubes should be labeled Salt, Sugar, Vinegar, and Horseradish. Pour the salt solution from the stock bottle into the test tube marked Salt up to the halfway point. In similar fashion, half fill the sugar tube with the sugar solution, the vinegar tube with the vinegar solution, and the horse-radish tube with the horseradish solution.

3. Prepare a tongue diagram for each subject tested; make as many copies of the Tongue Map on the next page as you will need. The recorder should write the subject's name, age, and gender on the tongue diagram.

4. Begin the experiment by having the subject rinse his or her mouth with bottled or tap water. Then, the experimenter will place a small amount of each of the four liquids on various areas of the tongue as indicated in the next few procedures. Remember that all the liquids are harmless.

(continued) 🔥

A Matter of Taste (Component 1: Taste Buds) *(continued)*

Tongue Map

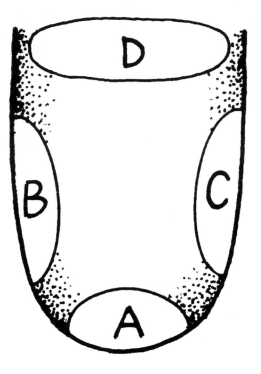

A Matter of Taste (Component 1: Taste Buds) *(continued)*

5. The experimenter should put on a pair of latex gloves. The subject should close his or her eyes and stick his or her tongue out.

6. The experimenter should dip a cotton swab into the salt test tube and should gently rub the subject's tongue in area A with the moistened swab. The subject should then be asked what taste or tastes he or she experiences. In the Data Collection and Analysis section and on the tongue map adjacent to area A, the recorder should write the taste that the subject named.

7. The subject should now rinse his or her mouth until no taste is sensed. Then the experimenter should swab area B with the salt solution and ask what taste is experienced. Repeat the rinsing and swabbing of the salt solution in areas C and D. For each swabbing, record the indicated taste in the Data Collection and Analysis section and on the tongue map. 🖐**Never dip a used swab into a stock bottle. Use only the test tube. Use one swab for each taste. Then discard it! Use a new set of test tubes for each subject.** The recorder will write the taste in the Data Collection and Analysis section and on the tongue map adjacent to areas B, C, and D.

8. Repeat steps 6 and 7, but use the sugar solution.

9. Repeat steps 6 and 7, but use the vinegar solution.

10. Repeat steps 6 and 7, but use the horseradish solution.

11. Switch roles, and repeat steps 5 through 7. For each new subject, change the order in which the solutions are presented. **Remember, the order should not be known by the subject**.

12. Switch roles again, and repeat steps 5 through 7.

DATA COLLECTION AND ANALYSIS

Salt solution

Subject name	Age	Gender	Taste sensed area A	Taste sensed area B	Taste sensed area C	Taste sensed area D
1.						
2.						
3.						

(continued)

Name _____   Date _____

Sugar solution

Subject name	Age	Gender	Taste sensed area A	Taste sensed area B	Taste sensed area C	Taste sensed area D
1.						
2.						
3.						

Vinegar solution

Subject name	Age	Gender	Taste sensed area A	Taste sensed area B	Taste sensed area C	Taste sensed area D
1.						
2.						
3.						

A Matter of Taste (Component 1: Taste Buds) *(continued)*

Horseradish solution

Subject name	Age	Gender	Taste sensed area A	Taste sensed area B	Taste sensed area C	Taste sensed area D
1.						
2.						
3.						

Pool your results with those from the rest of the class by placing them in a chart on the chalkboard.

1. Which area(s) sensed only one taste? _____

_____

2. Which area(s) sensed more than one taste? _____

_____

3. Which area appears to be the center for tasting salty food? _____

4. Which area seems to be the center for tasting sweet food? _____

5. Which area seems to be the center for tasting sour food? _____

6. Which area seems to be the center for tasting bitter food? _____

❔ CONCLUDING QUESTIONS

1. Based on the results of your experiment, are males or females more sensitive to sweet foods? What is the basis for your answer? _____

_____

2. Are females more sensitive than males to the taste of bitter foods? Justify your answer. _____

_____

_____

(continued)

A Matter of Taste (Component 1: Taste Buds) *(continued)*

3. Why are the taste buds that are located on the tip of the tongue the most important? _____

_____

_____

Indicate whether the following statement is true or false (use your data to defend your answer): "Any taste bud can detect any of the four basic tastes. However, some taste buds are more sensitive to one particular taste than to the others." _____

👉 Follow-up Activities 👈

1. Map the taste buds on several adults. How do your results compare?

2. Prepare weaker and weaker concentrations of a sugar solution. What is the lowest concentration at which a person reports a sweet taste?

3. Research the location of taste buds in fish and in insects. Report your findings to your classmates.

4. Research the relationship between the number of taste buds and taste perception. Report your results to the class.

(continued)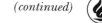

A Matter of Taste (Component 2: Smell)

✔ INSTRUCTIONAL OBJECTIVES

Students will be able to

- record and analyze data.
- conduct a controlled experiment.
- draw conclusions based upon data.

🌐 NATIONAL SCIENCE STANDARDS ADDRESSED

Students demonstrate an understanding of

- response to environmental stimuli.
- senses and behavior.
- big ideas and unifying concepts, such as cause and effect.

Students demonstrate scientific inquiry and problem-solving skills by

- working in teams to collect and share information.

✂ MATERIALS

For each group:

- Three pairs of latex or rubber gloves
- Blindfold
- Pen or pencil
- Toothpicks
- Small pieces of raw apple in a small plastic or paper cup
- Small pieces of raw turnip in a small plastic or paper cup
- Small pieces of raw pear in a small plastic or paper cup
- Small pieces of raw onion in a small plastic or paper cup
- Small pieces of strawberries in a small plastic or paper cup
- Paper napkins
- Tap water or bottled water
- Three clean plastic cups

Tongue

place food here

HELPFUL HINTS AND DISCUSSION

Time frame: One period
Structure: In cooperative learning groups of three students
Location: In class

The previous activity, "A Matter of Taste (Component 1: Taste Buds)," should be done before doing this activity. **It is important not to reuse a toothpick or insert a used toothpick into a cup of food that is to be used for testing other subjects.** Demonstrate the proper procedure for pinching the nose closed, and show the students where on the tongue to place the food. Students should avoid the areas of the tongue that were mapped in the previous activity. It is important to present the foods in a random order to all the subjects. Ask the students if they are allergic to apples, turnips, pears, onions, or strawberries. These students should NOT be used as test subjects.

ADAPTATIONS FOR HIGH AND LOW ACHIEVERS

High Achievers: These students should be encouraged to carry out the Follow-up Activities.

Low Achievers: These students may require instructions and practice to achieve the proper technique for placing the food on the tongue with a toothpick. A wall chart of the tongue should be used to illustrate the area of the tongue under investigation. These students should be required to work in cooperative learning groups composed of a mix of high and low achievers. Another possibility is to carry out this activity with the help of an educational aide.

SCORING RUBRIC

Full credit should be given to those students who record observations and who provide correct answers in full sentences to all the questions. Extra credit can be given if any of the Follow-up Activities are completed.

📖 INTERNET TIE-INS
http://www.htv.co.uk/wales/rhp/fshtm2/fsanosmi.html
http://www.campus.bt.com/public

❓ QUIZ
1. Explain why the flavor of a food becomes stronger as you chew it.
2. Explain why a person's sense of smell is an important survival mechanism.

Name _____   Date _____

A Matter of Taste (Component 2: Smell)

👆 BEFORE YOU BEGIN 👆

In using the taste map of the tongue in the previous activity, you may not have known that other senses play a role in determining taste. Smell plays a major role in your ability to taste. Consider the odor of foods that you don't like. You reject them even before you taste them. Taste and smell are two different senses that work together to affect the way we sense the flavor of foods and beverages. The sense of **taste** tells us if a food is salty, sweet, bitter, or sour, while **smell** senses gaseous chemicals given off by what we eat and drink.

Smell is very important in helping you define individual food flavors. When you chew and swallow food, air that carries these chemicals is forced to the rear of the mouth and nose. There, the chemicals come in contact with the smell detectors that most people associate with taste but that, in reality, are the sense of smell. The more you chew, the more gases that reach these **olfactory receptors**, or smell cells. If air can't reach the olfactory receptors, your sense of smell and taste will be lessened. This is why you can't taste very well when you have a cold.

In this activity, you will explore the important role that the sense of smell plays in our sense of taste.

✂ MATERIALS

For each group:

- Three pairs of latex or rubber gloves
- Blindfold
- Pen or pencil
- Toothpicks
- Small pieces of raw apple in a small plastic or paper cup
- Small pieces of raw turnip in a small plastic or paper cup
- Small pieces of raw pear in a small plastic or paper cup
- Small pieces of raw onion in a small plastic or paper cup
- Small pieces of strawberries in a small plastic or paper cup
- Paper napkins
- Tap water or bottled water
- Three clean plastic cups

📦 PROCEDURE

1. Work in teams of three students. You will take turns as the experimenter, the recorder, and the subject as you go through each repetition of this experiment.

2. If you are acting as the experimenter, blindfold the subject. Then, on the table, arrange the plastic cups of the listed foods.

3. Ask the subject to hold his or her nose closed with the thumb and forefinger of one hand.

4. Put on a pair of protective gloves. **Present the foods in a random order.** Using a toothpick, place a small amount of a food sample (for example, apple) in the center of the subject's tongue as shown in the diagram.

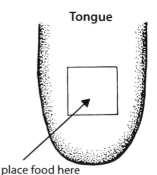

Tongue

place food here

(continued)

A Matter of Taste (Component 2: Smell) (continued)

Ask the subject to taste the sample; it can be chewed, **but not swallowed**. Ask the subject to name the food if possible. The subject should then spit the sample into a paper napkin and discard the napkin into the garbage pail. The experimenter should place each used toothpick in the garbage pail. In the Data Collection and Analysis section, the recorder should write the subject's answers.

5. Ask the subject to clean his or her mouth by rinsing with some fresh water before tasting another food sample.

6. Repeat steps 3 through 5, but use the four other foods in random order.

7. At this point, repeat the taste tests using the same foods with the same subject. However, this time make sure the subject stays blindfolded but is **not** holding his or her nose. Present the foods in the same order as you did when the nose was pinched closed. The recorder reports the findings in the Data Collection and Analysis section.

8. Change roles so that the recorder becomes the experimenter, the experimenter becomes the subject, and the subject becomes the recorder. Repeat steps 2 through 7 twice so that each team member has a chance to be the subject. Make sure to present the foods to each new subject in a different order. **BE SURE NOT TO SHARE TOOTHPICKS**.

DATA COLLECTION AND ANALYSIS

Subject 1 _____

	Nose Pinched—Food Reported	Nose Not Pinched—Food Reported
Turnip		
Apple		
Pear		
Onion		
Strawberry		

(continued)

A Matter of Taste (Component 2: Smell) *(continued)*

Subject 2 _____

	Nose Pinched—Food Reported	Nose Not Pinched—Food Reported
Turnip		
Apple		
Pear		
Onion		
Strawberry		

Subject 3 _____

	Nose Pinched—Food Reported	Nose Not Pinched—Food Reported
Turnip		
Apple		
Pear		
Onion		
Strawberry		

1. Were the data consistent for all three subjects? What is the basis for your answer? _____

_____

_____

2. Did the onion ever taste like a strawberry? _____ If so, under what circumstances?

_____

_____

3. How can you explain that with the nose pinched, the apple, turnip, and pear may
   have tasted alike?

_____

_____

(continued)

A Matter of Taste (Component 2: Smell) *(continued)*

❓ CONCLUDING QUESTIONS

1. Under what circumstances could the loss of a person's sense of smell be hazardous? _____

   _____

   _____

2. Which would you consider more important in determining the taste of a food: the taste buds or the smell receptors? State the reasons for your answer. _____

   _____

   _____

👃 Follow-up Activities 👃

1. Research the reasons that people may lose their sense of smell. Report your findings to your class.

2. Repeat the sense-of-smell procedures using warm foods, such as cooked meat or warm soup.

3. Repeat the sense-of-smell activities with subjects between 30 and 40 years old and between 50 and 60 years old. Test subjects who are over 60 years of age. What conclusions can you reach? Share your data with your classmates.

A Matter of Taste (Component 3: Irritants)

✔ INSTRUCTIONAL OBJECTIVES

Students will be able to

- record and analyze data.
- conduct a controlled experiment.
- draw conclusions based upon data.

🌐 NATIONAL SCIENCE STANDARDS ADDRESSED

Students demonstrate an understanding of

- response to environmental stimuli.
- senses and behavior.
- big ideas and unifying concepts, such as cause and effect.

Students demonstrate scientific inquiry and problem-solving skills by

- working in teams to collect and share information.

✂ MATERIALS

For each group:

- Three pairs of latex or rubber gloves
- Blindfold
- Pen or pencil
- Mustard in a small cup
- White horseradish in a small cup
- Ginger in a small cup
- Black pepper in a small cup
- Three clean plastic cups
- Tap water or bottled water
- 12 plastic teaspoons
- Paper napkins

HELPFUL HINTS AND DISCUSSION

Time frame: One period
Structure: In cooperative learning groups of three students
Location: In class

✋ **Stress that students should not reuse any spoons or insert a used spoon in a food sample cup.** If a student finds the food sample too irritating, the testing of that subject should be stopped, and the subject's mouth should be rinsed with water immediately. Use a wall chart of the tongue or the diagram on page 71 to illustrate where the food samples are to be placed.

ADAPTATIONS FOR HIGH AND LOW ACHIEVERS

High Achievers: These students should be encouraged to carry out the Follow-up Activities and to assist the low achievers in their cooperative learning group.

Low Achievers: These students may require instructions and practice to achieve the proper technique for placing the food on the tongue. These students should work in cooperative learning groups composed of a mix of high and low achievers. Another possibility is to carry out this activity with the help of an educational aide.

SCORING RUBRIC

Full credit should be given to those students who record observations and who provide correct answers in full sentences to all the questions. Extra credit can be given if any of the Follow-up Activities are completed.

💻 INTERNET TIE-INS

http://www.campus.bt.com/public/Science Net/database/Social/Senses/s0170c.html
http://ificinfo.health.org/insight/exper.htm
http://1138.214.184.12/sn_arc97/7_12_97/bob1.html

❓ QUIZ

1. Explain why the tongue is an important organ in selecting foods.
2. Why is it beneficial for the pain receptors on the tongue to be located in the papillae?

A Matter of Taste (Component 3: Irritants)

✋ BEFORE YOU BEGIN ✋

In this activity, you will investigate the role that pain has upon taste. Some foods and beverages irritate the pain receptors in the papillae (taste buds) on the tongue. These pain receptors are actually wrapped around the taste buds. Foods such as ginger and black pepper contain irritants that are "hot"—that is, they cause a burning sensation. Foods eaten when very cold, such as ice cream, also irritate the pain receptors. In this activity, you will taste a few foods with chemical irritants to determine whether these irritants affect the other components of taste, particularly smell.

✂ MATERIALS

For each group:
- Three pairs of latex or rubber gloves
- Blindfold
- Pen or pencil
- Mustard in a small cup
- White horseradish in a small cup
- Ginger in a small cup

- Black pepper in a small cup
- Three clean plastic cups
- Tap water or bottled water
- 12 plastic teaspoons
- Paper napkins

◈ PROCEDURE

1. Work in teams of three students. You will take turns as the experimenter, the recorder, and the subject as you go through each repetition of the experiment.

2. If you are the experimenter, blindfold the subject. Then, on the table, arrange the plastic cups of listed foods in random order. This is important!

3. Ask the subject to hold his or her nose closed with the thumb and forefinger of one hand.

Tongue

place food here

4. Put on a pair of protective gloves. Using a plastic spoon, place a very small amount of one of the food samples (for example, mustard) on the center of the subject's tongue as shown in the diagram. Avoid placing the food on the front, sides, or back of the tongue. Ask the subject to taste the food but not to swallow it, and to state the name of the food (if possible) and any sensation, such as "burning" or "hot." The subject should then spit the food into a paper napkin and discard the napkin in the garbage pail. The used spoon should be placed in the garbage pail by the experimenter. In the Data Collection and Analysis section, the recorder should write the subject's comments.

5. Ask the subject to clean his or her mouth by rinsing with some fresh water before tasting another listed food sample.

6. Repeat steps 3 through 5, using all the other food samples.

(continued)

A Matter of Taste (Component 3: Irritants) *(continued)*

7. At this point, using the same subject, repeat the taste tests in the same order. However, this time the subject should be blindfolded but should not be holding his or her nose. In the Data Collection and Analysis section, report the findings.

8. Change roles so that the recorder becomes the experimenter, the experimenter becomes the subject, and the subject becomes the recorder. Repeat steps 2 through 7 two times so that each team member can be the subject. These subjects should taste the various foods in a random order.

DATA COLLECTION AND ANALYSIS

Subject 1 _____

Food Tested	Nose Pinched		Blindfolded, Nose Not Pinched	
	Food Named	Sensation	Food Named	Sensation
Mustard				
Black pepper				
Horseradish				
Ginger				

Subject 2 _____

Food Tested	Nose Pinched		Blindfolded, Nose Not Pinched	
	Food Named	Sensation	Food Named	Sensation
Mustard				
Black pepper				
Horseradish				
Ginger				

Subject 3 _____

Food Tested	Nose Pinched		Blindfolded, Nose Not Pinched	
	Food Named	Sensation	Food Named	Sensation
Mustard				
Black pepper				
Horseradish				
Ginger				

(continued)

A Matter of Taste (Component 3: Irritants) *(continued)*

What effect did pinching the nose have upon irritation of the pain receptors in the tongue? Justify your answer.

_____

_____

_____

❓ CONCLUDING QUESTIONS

1. Which of the three components of taste do you think is the most important? Why? _____

_____

_____

2. Why can very cold foods, such as frozen ice cream, be considered irritants? _____

_____

_____

3. Name foods—others than those used in this activity—that "bring tears to your eyes" when eaten.

_____

_____

_____

_____

👆 Follow-up Activities 👆

1. Research why a nonalcoholic beer can never taste the same as beer made with alcohol. (**Hint:** Search the Internet for information on how alcohol affects the three components of taste.) Report your findings to the class.

2. Prepare a report that explains why some people enjoy eating spicy foods, while others, at the first bite, gulp down water.

3. Do a library or Internet search for an explanation of "transient desensitization" as it affects the eating of spicy foods.

Measuring Vital Capacity by Water Displacement

✔ INSTRUCTIONAL OBJECTIVES

Students will be able to

- record and analyze data.
- draw conclusions based upon data.
- compare predicted results with actual results.
- explain relationships of age, gender, and height to vital capacity of the lungs.

🌐 NATIONAL SCIENCE STANDARDS ADDRESSED

Students demonstrate an understanding of

- structure and function in living systems.
- big ideas and unifying concepts, such as cause and effect.

Students demonstrate scientific inquiry and problem-solving skills by

- identifying problems.
- working in teams to collect data.
- using evidence from reliable sources to develop a model.

Students demonstrate competence with the tools of science by

- using scientific equipment.

✂ MATERIALS

For each group:

- Two glass or plastic jars (1 gallon [3780 ml])
- Glass plate to seal opening of the jar
- 50-cm length of rubber tubing
- Mouthpieces (sterilized glass tubes, 7 cm in length, that fit snugly into the rubber tubing)
- Water
- Pneumatic trough
- 1-liter graduated cylinder
- 70% alcohol
- Gauze pads
- Paper towels

💻 INTERNET TIE-INS

http://human.physiol.arizona.edu
http://www.utep.edu/~anatomy/lectures/resp.html
http://syllabus.syr.edu/SPP/Coltonr/SPP215/resphys.htm
http://129.255.168.54/Providers/ClinRef/FPHandbook/Chapter03/06-3.html

❓ QUIZ

1. Why is knowing a person's vital capacity important?
2. Name a medical condition that would reduce a person's vital capacity.

HELPFUL HINTS AND DISCUSSION

Time frame: One to two periods
Structure: In cooperative learning groups
Location: In class

Discuss and demonstrate how to set up the equipment as shown in the diagrams in the Student Activity pages. **Stress the importance of not sharing mouthpieces and demonstrate how to clean the mouthpieces before and after use with the alcohol-soaked gauze pad.** Discuss the use of the formulas for the computations of the predicted vital capacity.

ADAPTATIONS FOR HIGH AND LOW ACHIEVERS

High Achievers: These students should be encouraged to carry out the Follow-up Activities. They also should assist the low achievers with carrying out this activity and collecting and analyzing the data.

Low Achievers: These students should be helped with the mathematical tasks and should be carefully supervised when they are handling the equipment.

SCORING RUBRIC

Full credit should be given to those students who record the data correctly and who do the mathematics correctly. They should also answer all of the Concluding Questions. Extra credit can be given if any of the Follow-up Activities are completed.

Name _____ Date _____

Measuring Vital Capacity by Water Displacement

✋ BEFORE YOU BEGIN ✋

Did you ever wonder how much air you could exhale if you really tried? In this activity, you will get the answer. You will measure the maximum volume of air that moves out of your lungs after taking the deepest breath you can. This volume is called your **vital capacity**. However, before measuring your vital capacity, you will mathematically determine the average predicted vital capacity for a person of your gender, age, and height. Then, you will compare the predicted vital capacity with your own actual capacity.

✂ MATERIALS

For each group:

- Two glass or plastic jars (1 gallon [3780 ml])
- Glass plate to seal opening of the jar
- 50-cm length of rubber tubing
- Mouthpieces (sterilized glass tubes, 7 cm in length, that fit snugly into the rubber tubing)

- Water
- Pneumatic trough
- 1-liter graduated cylinder
- 70% alcohol
- Gauze pads
- Paper towels

PROCEDURE

1. The formula for predicting an average value for the vital capacity in milliliters is slightly different for males and females.

Males = 27.6 – (0.11 × age [in years]) × height (in cm)*

Females = 21.8 – (0.1 × age [in years]) × height (in cm)*

Substitute your age and height in the formula for your gender in order to determine your predicted vital capacity. The answer will be in milliliters (ml). Record your answer and those of your learning group in the Data Collection and Analysis section. To help you, here is a sample predicted vital capacity worked out for you. The subject is a girl, $13\frac{1}{2}$ years old, who is 5 feet tall.

$$21.8 - (0.1 \times 13.5) \times (5 \times 30) = x$$

$$21.8 - 1.35 \times 150 = x$$

$$20.45 \times 150 = 3067.5 \text{ ml}$$

2. Now you will determine your true vital capacity by doing the following. First, fill one jar completely with water and cover its opening with the glass plate. Set the jar aside for the moment. Next, insert a clean mouthpiece into one end of the rubber tubing. Place the mouthpiece on a clean gauze pad in a safe place for now.

---

* 1 foot = 30 cm

(continued)

Measuring Vital Capacity by Water Displacement *(continued)*

3. Place the other jar next to the pneumatic trough so that any water that overflows from the trough will fall into it. Fill the pneumatic trough with sufficient water so that a small amount flows out of the trough into the jar.

4. Carefully pick up the covered jar. While holding the cover with one hand, place the other hand around the body of the jar, invert the jar, and place the jar on the shelf in the trough. Be sure the jar's opening is over one of the holes in the shelf. Now, gently and carefully remove the glass plate that is between the shelf and the jar.

5. Insert the rubber end of the tubing into the jar by passing it through the hole in the shelf as shown in Diagram 1.

Diagram 1

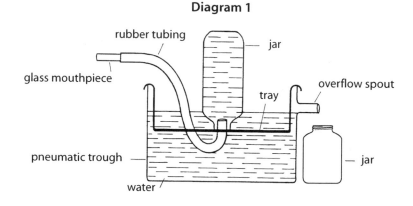

6. Empty the other jar and dry it thoroughly with a piece of paper towel. Replace it beneath the overflow spout.

7. Clean off the mouthpiece with a piece of gauze that has been dipped in the alcohol. Wait a few minutes for the alcohol to evaporate. Take in *one* breath, bringing into your lungs as much air as you can. Hold the air in; then put the mouthpiece to your lips and exhale as much air as you can into the rubber tube as indicated in Diagram 2. When you have exhaled as much air as possible, remove the mouthpiece from the rubber tube and clean it with another alcohol-soaked gauze pad.

Diagram 2

8. Take the water collected in the jar under the overflow tube and pour it into the graduated cylinder. Determine the number of milliliters, and record the amount in the Data Collection and Analysis section.

9. Repeat steps 2 through 8 for the other members of your learning group.

10. Include your data in a master chart on the chalkboard.

(continued)

Measuring Vital Capacity by Water Displacement *(continued)*

DATA COLLECTION AND ANALYSIS

Subject	Gender	Age	Height in Centimeters	Predicted Vital Capacity	Measured Vital Capacity

How accurate were the predicted vital capacities when compared with the actual amounts?

_____

What is the evidence for your answer? _____

_____

CONCLUDING QUESTIONS

1. Based upon the data collected by the entire class, is your answer to the question in the Data Collection and Analysis section the same as before? Defend your answer. _____

_____

_____

2. Based on the entire class's data, which is the more important factor in determining vital capacity: age or height? Justify your answer. _____

_____

_____

👆 Follow-up Activities 👆

1. Use a spirometer to measure **tidal volume**, **expiratory reserve volume**, and **residual volume** of the members of your learning group. Look up these terms in a research library before doing this activity.

2. Research what causes a person to "have his breath knocked out." Is this phrase scientifically accurate? Explain your answer and report your work to the class.

3. Research the effects of smoking upon vital capacity and other lung capacities and volumes. Report your findings to the class.

Measuring Lung Volumes by Using Balloons

✔ INSTRUCTIONAL OBJECTIVES

Students will be able to

- record and analyze data.
- draw conclusions based upon data.
- compare predicted results with actual results.
- explain relationships among vital capacity, tidal volume, and expiratory reserve volume of the lungs.

🌐 NATIONAL SCIENCE STANDARDS ADDRESSED

Students demonstrate an understanding of

- structure and function in living systems.
- big ideas and unifying concepts, such as cause and effect.

Students demonstrate scientific inquiry and problem-solving skills by

- identifying problems.
- working in teams to collect data.
- using evidence from reliable sources to develop a model.

Students demonstrate competence with the tools of science by

- using scientific equipment.

✂ MATERIALS

- Bow calipers
- Large round balloons
- Metric ruler

calipers

metric ruler

HELPFUL HINTS AND DISCUSSION

Time frame: One to two periods
Structure: In cooperative learning groups
Location: In class

Emphasize the importance of not sharing balloons among learning group members. Review the mathematical equations used in this activity. Discuss the difficulty in maintaining a normal breathing pattern when you are concentrating upon breathing normally. Prepare several large charts on the chalkboard so that the data of the entire class can be analyzed and reviewed.

ADAPTATIONS FOR HIGH AND LOW ACHIEVERS

High Achievers: These students should be encouraged to carry out the Follow-up Activities. They also should assist the low achievers with carrying out this activity and with collecting and analyzing the data.

Low Achievers: These students should be helped with the mathematical tasks and should be carefully supervised when they are handling the balloons.

SCORING RUBRIC

Full credit should be given to those students who record the data correctly and who do the mathematics correctly. They also should answer all of the Concluding Questions. Extra credit can be given if any of the Follow-up Activities are completed.

🖥 INTERNET TIE-INS

http://human.physiol.arizona.edu/SCHED/Respiration/MorganPFLab/Station1.html
http://www.utep.edu/~anatomy/lectures/resp.html
http://syllabus.syr.edu/SPP/Coltonr/SPP215/resphys.htm
http://129.255.168.54/Providers/ClinRef/FPHandbook/Chapter03/06-3.html

❓ QUIZ

1. What is the difference between vital capacity and tidal volume?
2. What is meant by the phrase *expiratory reserve volume?*

Measuring Lung Volumes by Using Balloons

👆 BEFORE YOU BEGIN 👆

In another activity, you measured your vital capacity by displacing water. In this activity, you will once again measure and compare your vital capacity, this time by filling a balloon with air. Using balloons will also allow you to measure your **tidal volume**, which is the amount of air inhaled and exhaled during one normal respiration, and your **expiratory reserve volume**, which is the amount of air you exhale after a normal exhalation. For many people, the expiratory reserve volume is approximately 25 percent of their vital capacity. Finally, this percentage will be determined for you and the other members of your learning group.

Each team member must use his or her own balloon for this activity. **There is to be NO sharing of balloons!** The most difficult part of this activity is to breathe normally for determining both tidal volume and expiratory reserve volume. Most people alter their breathing when asked to breathe normally. This is because breathing is controlled both consciously and unconsciously by the brain through a complex system of nerves. Do your best to inhale and exhale a normal amount when told to do so.

✂ MATERIALS

- Bow calipers
- Large round balloons
- Metric ruler

📦 PROCEDURE

- Each member of the team will take turns acting as the experimenter, recorder, and subject. Each team member is to inflate and deflate his or her balloon at least 10 times before proceeding. Remember, do not blow into a balloon that someone else has used.

Part 1: Vital Capacity

A. In the space provided in the Data Collection and Analysis section, Part 1, record the vital capacity that you calculated for yourself with the water displacement method. This was determined in the activity "Measuring Vital Capacity by Water Displacement." If you did not carry out that activity, it is not necessary to do so at this time. Leave that space in the Data Collection and Analysis section blank.

B. To determine your vital capacity using balloons, do the following:

1) The experimenter should ask the subject to inhale as deep a breath as possible and then to hold that breath.

2) While holding the stretched balloon by the round end, the experimenter should quickly place the subject's stretched balloon (which has had all the air pressed out of it) into the subject's mouth.

(continued) 🔥

Measuring Lung Volumes by Using Balloons *(continued)*

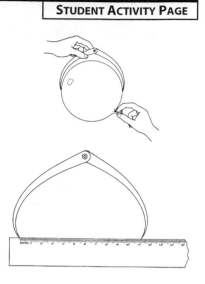

3) The experimenter should ask the subject to exhale as much air as possible into the balloon. The subject should then close the opening of the balloon by tightly holding it closed with the thumb and forefinger of one hand.

4) The experimenter should use the calipers to determine the diameter of the balloon at its widest point. After this is done, the subject may release the air from the balloon. The experimenter should measure the diameter of the balloon in centimeters by placing the ends of the calipers on the metric ruler as shown in the diagram on the right. The recorder will enter that number in the Data Collection and Analysis section.

5) The recorder should determine the subject's vital capacity by using the formula for determining the volume of a sphere, which is as follows:

$$\text{volume} = \frac{4}{3}\pi\frac{\text{diameter}^3}{2} = \frac{4}{3} \times 3.1417 \times \frac{\text{diameter}^3}{2} = \text{volume in cubic centimeters}$$

*π = 3.1417	1 cubic centimeter = 1 milliliter

6) Then, the recorder should enter the volume in milliliters in the Data Collection and Analysis section.

Part 2: Tidal Volume

A. The subject should have his or her tidal volume measured four times and the average used for best results.

B. Ask the subject to breathe in **normally**. After inhaling a normal amount of air, the subject should then insert the balloon opening into his or her mouth and exhale **normally** into the balloon.

C. After each trial, the experimenter should measure the diameter of the balloon with the calipers and ruler in the same manner as was done for measuring the vital capacity of the lungs. Then, the recorder should use the formula for determining the volume of a sphere, which is as follows:

$$\text{volume} = \frac{4}{3}\pi\frac{\text{diameter}^3}{2} = \frac{4}{3} \times 3.1417 \times \frac{\text{diameter}^3}{2} = \text{volume in cubic centimeters}$$

*π = 3.1417	1 cubic centimeter = 1 milliliter

D. The recorder will write the tidal volume of the lungs in milliliters in the Data Collection and Analysis section, Part 2.

E. Scientists estimate that the tidal volume for young people is 7.5 ml per kilogram (kg) of body weight. One pound is equal to 0.45 kilograms. Multiply your body weight in pounds by 0.45, then multiply that amount by 7.5 ml. Insert the answer in the last column in the chart in the Data Collection and Analysis section.

(continued)

Measuring Lung Volumes by Using Balloons *(continued)*

Part 3: Expiratory Reserve Volume

A. The subject should have his or her expiratory reserve volume measured four times and the average used.

B. The subject should breathe normally for a minute. Then, after taking a normal breath, the subject should exhale normally, hold his or her breath, and quickly insert the opening of the balloon into his or her mouth. The subject should continue to exhale as much air as possible into the balloon. The balloon should be sealed as before, and then the subject should breathe normally.

C. The experimenter or the recorder should follow the Procedures, Part 2, for measuring the diameter of the balloon and converting cubic centimeters into milliliters.

D. In many cases the expiratory reserve volume is $\frac{1}{4}$, or 25 percent, of the vital capacity. To arrive at this ratio, divide the expiratory reserve volume by the vital capacity found by the balloon method and multiply by 100.

$$\frac{\text{expiratory reserve volume}}{\text{vital capacity (balloon method)}} \times 100 = \%$$

E. In the Data Collection and Analysis section, Part 3, the recorder should enter the data in the appropriate columns in the table.

• Repeat the three procedures with the other members of your learning group.

• Include your data in a master chart on the chalkboard.

DATA COLLECTION AND ANALYSIS

Part 1: Vital Capacity

1. What is your vital capacity as measured by water displaced? _____

2. What is your vital capacity as measured by the balloon method? _____ .

3. How can you explain any differences between the two numbers? _____

_____

4. Which method is more accurate? _____ What are your reasons for your answer?

_____

_____

Part 2: Tidal Volume

Subject	Trial 1 (ml)	Trial 2 (ml)	Trial 3 (ml)	Trial 4 (ml)	Average (ml)	Estimated Tidal Volume (ml)

(continued)

Measuring Lung Volumes by Using Balloons *(continued)*

Part 3: Expiratory Reserve Volume

Subject	Trial 1 (ml)	Trial 2 (ml)	Trial 3 (ml)	Trial 4 (ml)	Average (ml)	Estimated Tidal Volume (ml)

1. How do your percentages compare with the average for most people, which is 25%?

❓ CONCLUDING QUESTIONS

1. What are the possible causes for errors in this activity? _____

_____

_____

2. Of what value to physicians is the information regarding lung volumes and capacity? _____

_____

_____

👈 Follow-up Activities 👈

1. Use a spirometer to measure inspiratory reserve volume, functional residual volume, and total lung capacity of the members of your learning group.

2. Research alveolar ventilation and the presence of dead space in the lungs. Report your results to the class.

3. Research the theories of gas exchange within lungs.

Do Antioxidants Preserve Fresh Fruits and Vegetables?

✔ INSTRUCTIONAL OBJECTIVES

Students will be able to

- record and analyze data.
- draw conclusions based upon data.
- determine if antioxidants are preservatives for fresh fruits and vegetables.
- compare the preservative effects of vitamins A, C, and E.

🌐 NATIONAL SCIENCE STANDARDS ADDRESSED

Students demonstrate an understanding of

- the properties of matter.
- big ideas and unifying concepts, such as cause and effect.
- the impact of technology.

Students demonstrate scientific inquiry and problem-solving skills by

- identifying problems.
- working in teams to collect data.

Students demonstrate competence with the tools of science by

- using scientific equipment.
- collecting and analyzing data.

✂ MATERIALS

- Vitamin A capsules (25,000 International Units)
- Vitamin C tablets (250 mg)
- Vitamin E capsules (400 International Units)
- Three fresh, unbruised fruits that are readily available (apples, pears, peaches, strawberries)
- Three fresh, unbruised vegetables that are readily available (potatoes, squash, peas, beans)
- Five petri dishes per fruit and vegetable tested
- Labels
- Marking crayon
- Distilled water
- 🖐 Sharp knife

🖐 = Safety icon

HELPFUL HINTS AND DISCUSSION

Time frame: One week to eight school days
Structure: In cooperative learning groups
Location: In class

Prepare the vitamin solutions as follows:

- Vitamin A solution: dissolve four 25,000-International Unit capsules in 100 ml of mineral oil.
- Vitamin C solution: dissolve four 250-mg tablets in 100 ml of distilled or deionized water.
- Vitamin E solution: dissolve six 400-International Unit capsules in 100 ml of mineral oil.

Teacher should stress the importance of keeping the fruit and vegetable slices covered with the appropriate solution—except, of course, for the petri dish halves exposed to the air. Start this activity on the first day of a school week that has no holidays. 🖐**Instruct students in the proper procedure for cutting the fruits and vegetables. Warn the students that this phase must be done under a teacher's or another adult's supervision.**

ADAPTATIONS FOR HIGH AND LOW ACHIEVERS

High Achievers: These students should be encouraged to carry out the Follow-up Activities. They should assist the low achievers with carrying out this activity and collecting and analyzing the data.

Low Achievers: These students should be helped and carefully supervised when preparing the slices for this activity.

SCORING RUBRIC

Full credit should be given to those students who record the data correctly. They should answer all of the Concluding Questions and the analysis question. Extra credit can be given if any of the Follow-up Activities are completed.

 **INTERNET TIE-INS**   http://www333.hmc.edu/~clewis/aging/background.html
http://www.lametcoeu.com/biocell3.htm

QUIZ   1. Why are free radicals harmful?
2. What is the role of antioxidants in the aging process?

Name _____   Date _____

Do Antioxidants Preserve Fresh Fruits and Vegetables?

BEFORE YOU BEGIN

Free radicals are uncharged atoms or molecules that have an odd number of very reactive electrons. Free radicals that contain oxygen (known as **oxygen-free radicals**) can destroy or damage cells and are involved in the aging process. Oxygen-free radicals cannot be avoided. They are everywhere in our environment. In addition, however, there are naturally occurring antioxidants. These are chemical compounds that slow down cell damage by oxygen-free radicals.

Vitamin A, vitamin C, and vitamin E are three naturally occurring antioxidants. In this activity, you will use these antioxidants to slow down the aging of plant cells caused by oxygen-free radicals. You will also find out if this makes fruits and vegetables last longer before spoiling.

MATERIALS

- Vitamin A solution
- Vitamin C solution
- Vitamin E solution
- Three fresh, unbruised fruits that are readily available (apples, pears, peaches, strawberries)
- Three fresh, unbruised vegetables that are readily available (potatoes, squash, peas, beans)

- Five petri dishes per fruit or vegetable tested
- Labels
- Marking crayon
- Distilled water
- Sharp knife

= Safety icon

PROCEDURE

1. Prepare five labels for each fruit and vegetable you will be using in this activity. Write the name of the fruit or vegetable on each label. In addition, write "Vitamin A" on one label, "Vitamin C" on the second, "Vitamin E" on the third, "Water" on the fourth, and "Air" on the last label. Paste these labels on the outside of each petri dish half.

2. Use the knife to prepare five equal slices of each fruit and vegetable that will be tested. Place one slice in a half petri dish. **This step must be done under the supervision of your teacher or another adult.**

3. Cover the slice in the "Vitamin A" dish with vitamin A solution. In similar fashion, cover the remaining four slices with whatever solution is named on the petri dish label. Cover the "Vitamin C" slice with vitamin C solution, and so on. Do nothing with the slice that is in the "Air" dish, but leave it exposed to the air.

(continued)

Do Antioxidants Preserve Fresh Fruits and Vegetables? *(continued)*

4. Leave the dishes exposed to the air in a safe place and examine them on a daily basis. Add fresh solution when necessary. Make sure all slices except the "Air" slices are covered with liquid at all times. Look for signs of decay or mold. When a dish shows evidence of decay or mold, record the number of days that have gone by since the start of the activity in the Data Collection and Analysis section. Discard the rotting slice of fruit or vegetable. Continue this activity until all slices have been discarded.

DATA COLLECTION AND ANALYSIS

Fruit or Vegetable	Vitamin A	Vitamin C	Vitamin E	Water	Air

Which covering (liquid) protected the fruits and vegetables the best? _____

CONCLUDING QUESTIONS

1. Based upon your data, do antioxidants preserve fresh fruits and vegetables? What are the reasons for your answer? _____

   _____

2. Why were two controls used in this activity? _____

   _____

   _____

👋 Follow-up Activities 👋

1. Repeat this activity, but cover the petri dish halves with clear plastic wrap. How do the results compare?

2. Research the use of BHT (butylated hydroxytoluene) and BHA (butylated hydroxyanisole) as preservatives for breads, cereal, nuts, and vegetable oils.

Muscle Marathon

✔ INSTRUCTIONAL OBJECTIVES

Students will be able to

- record and analyze data.
- draw conclusions based upon data.
- explain the cause of muscle fatigue.

🌐 NATIONAL SCIENCE STANDARDS ADDRESSED

Students demonstrate an understanding of

- good health, such as the benefits of exercise.
- biological functions in living systems.
- regulation and behavior of body systems.
- critical-thinking and unifying concepts, such as cause and effect.

Students demonstrate scientific inquiry and problem-solving skills by

- distinguishing between causes and effects.
- identifying problems.
- working collectively to gather data.

Students demonstrate competence with the tools of science by

- using scientific equipment accurately and responsibly.

✂ MATERIALS

- stopwatch or watch with a sweep second hand

HELPFUL HINTS AND DISCUSSION

Time frame: One to two class periods
Structure: In cooperative learning groups of three students
Location: In class

The focus of this activity is the striated muscles in the forearm which cause the fingers to open and close. In the first part of this activity, students will experience feelings of fatigue in these muscles due to lactic acid accumulation. They will probably determine that the muscles of one arm fatigue at a faster rate than muscles in the other arm. This can be related to a corresponding lack of muscle mass in the weaker arm. In the second part of the activity, students will try to determine whether increasing the oxygen content of blood by deep breathing will retard lactic acid production. You may wish to discuss degrading glucose with and without oxygen as well as glycolysis in muscle cells.

Although the arm exercise involved is relatively mild (opening and closing of the fists), **make sure that your students do not have any physical conditions that would make this activity risky.**

ADAPTATIONS FOR HIGH AND LOW ACHIEVERS

High Achievers: These students should be encouraged to carry out the Follow-up Activities. They should also answer all the Concluding Questions and perform the Follow-up Activities.

Low Achievers: These students should be helped in graphing and using the stopwatch.

SCORING RUBRIC

Full credit should be given to students who record observations and provide correct answers in full sentences to the questions. Extra credit can be given if any of the Follow-up Activities are completed.

🖥 INTERNET TIE-INS

http://www.dadechemistry.com/clinicalhtm/lactic2.htm
http://lactate.com/lact1a.html
http://www.brianmac.demon.co.uk/lactic.htm

❓ QUIZ

1. Describe how muscles become tired or sore.
2. Describe two ways in which lactic acid is removed from the muscles.

Muscle Marathon

BEFORE YOU BEGIN

Your body contains three kinds of muscles: heart muscle, involuntary muscle, and voluntary muscle. Your heart muscle and the involuntary muscles in your intestines and other parts of your body are not under your control. However, your voluntary muscles can be controlled. These muscles are attached to your bones; they move bones so that you can walk, sit, turn the pages of a book, work a computer keyboard, and so on. Voluntary muscles in your arm will be the subject of this activity.

If you have ever done any strenuous physical exercise, you have probably noticed that you get a tired feeling in your muscles. Your muscles may have even felt sore afterward. The tired feeling and soreness are due to the accumulation of **lactic acid** in the working muscles. When you stop exercising, your body has time to eliminate much of the lactic acid. Some is carried in the blood to your liver, where it combines with oxygen and changes to a helpful chemical compound. The lactic acid left in the muscles is mixed with oxygen that is brought to the muscles in your blood. This creates a compound called **pyruvate**. Pyruvate does not produce a tired or sore feeling.

You and your learning group will investigate two key questions:
- Which forearm gets **fatigued** (tired) faster?
- Since oxygen changes lactic acid into other compounds, will deep breathing (taking in more oxygen) increase the time you can exercise before fatigue sets in?

MATERIALS
- Stopwatch or watch with a sweep second hand

PROCEDURE

NOTE: If you have any physical disabilities which prevent you from engaging in strenuous exercise or breathing deeply, to not attempt to do this activity.

Part A

1. Appoint one member of your learning group to be the timekeeper. Select another member to be the counter and recorder. The third team member will be the subject.
2. The subject is to stand erect and raise his or her left hand to shoulder level, palm facing the floor, and maintain that position.
3. At the signal from the timekeeper, the subject will open and close his or her left hand as quickly and as often as possible for 20 seconds. The recorder will count the number of fists that are made by the subject.
4. At the end of 20 seconds, the timekeeper will announce, "Time." The subject will stop making fists. The recorder will enter the number of fists made in Date Table 1 in the Data Collection and Analysis section. The timekeeper should continue to keep time, allowing the subject 20 seconds of rest. Then the subject should repeat steps 2 through 4 **four additional times**.
5. Using his or her right hand, the subject should repeat steps 2 through 4.
6. Team members should switch roles twice in order for each team member to have a turn as the subject. Repeat steps 2 through 5 for each new subject.

(continued)

Muscle Marathon (continued)

Part B

NOTE: This part should not be started until each subject has rested his or her hands for at least 15 minutes. It may be necessary to do Part B on the school day following the completion of Part A.

1. Start with the person who was the first subject in Part A. The other team members are to assume the roles of timekeeper and record keeper.

2. The subject is to stand erect and raise his or her left hand to shoulder level, palm facing the floor, and maintain that position. He or she should start to take deep breaths, breathing in and out as deeply as possible at a normal, comfortable rate. Deep breathing is important rather than a rapid rate of breathing.

3. At the signal from the timekeeper, the subject will open and close his or her left hand as quickly and as often as possible for 20 seconds **while continuing to breathe deeply**. The recorder will count the number of fists that are made by the subject.

4. At the end of 20 seconds, the timekeeper will announce, "Time." The subject will stop making fists. The recorder will enter the number of fists made in Data Table 2 in the Data Collection and Analysis section. The timekeeper should continue to keep time, allowing the subject 20 seconds of rest. However, the subject should continue to breathe deeply. At the end of 20 seconds, the subject is to repeat steps 2 through 4 **four additional times**.

5. Using his or her right hand, the subject should repeat steps 2 through 4.

6. Team members should switch roles twice in order for each team member to have a turn being the subject. Repeat steps 2 through 5 for each new subject.

DATA COLLECTION AND ANALYSIS

DATA TABLE 1—Normal Breathing

Name of subject	Trial 1 # of fists made	Trial 2 # of fists made	Trial 3 # of fists made	Trial 4 # of fists made	Trial 5 # of fists made

DATA TABLE 2—Deep Breathing

Name of subject	Trial 1 # of fists made	Trial 2 # of fists made	Trial 3 # of fists made	Trial 4 # of fists made	Trial 5 # of fists made

(continued)

Name _____ Date _____

Muscle Marathon *(continued)*

In the space below, prepare a graph for each subject. Plot the results for normal and deep breathing on the same graph. Use one color for recording normal breathing and another color for recording deep breathing.

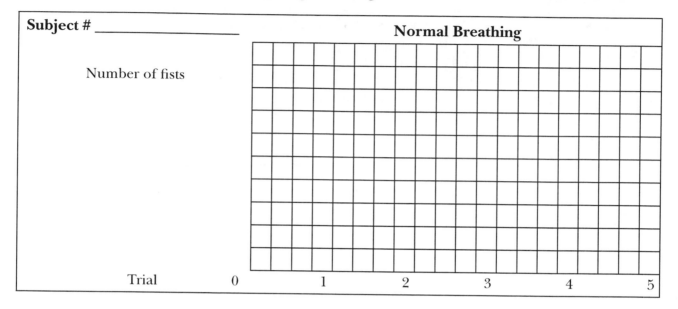

Subject # _____

Normal Breathing

Number of fists

Trial   0   1   2   3   4   5

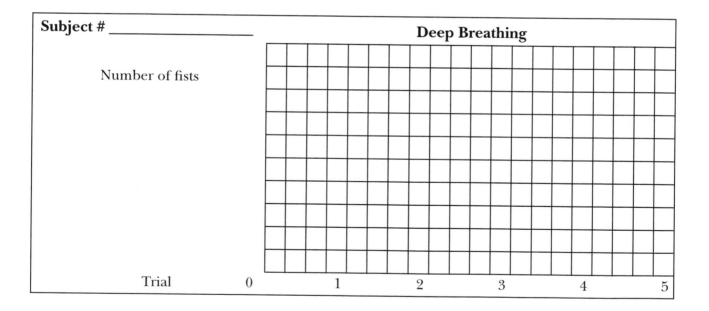

Subject # _____

Deep Breathing

Number of fists

Trial   0   1   2   3   4   5

(continued)

Muscle Marathon *(continued)*

1. Which hand was the stronger? How do you account for this? _____

_____

2. What effect did deep breathing have upon tiring of the arm muscles? What is your evidence?

_____

_____

_____

? CONCLUDING QUESTIONS

1. Why do fighters in a boxing match take deep breaths between rounds? _____

_____

_____

_____

2. Based on this activity, what advice would you give to a person who is planning
   to run in a marathon? _____

_____

_____

_____

👉 Follow-up Activities 👉

1. Research the role of the ATP and pyruvate in muscle action.

2. Repeat this activity using your lower limbs. How do the results compare with those you recorded using your hands?

3. Research the topic of "oxygen debt" and present your results to the class.

4. Research the topic of glycolysis in muscle tissue. Submit an article about this subject to the school newspaper.

(continued)

We want to hear from you! Your valuable comments and suggestions will help us meet your current and future classroom needs.

Your name_____Date_____

School name_____Phone_____

School address_____

Grade level taught_____Subject area(s) taught_____Average class size_____

Where did you purchase this publication?_____

Was your salesperson knowledgeable about this product?   Yes_____   No_____

What monies were used to purchase this product?

___School supplemental budget   ___Federal/state funding   ___Personal

Please "grade" this Walch publication according to the following criteria:

	A	B	C	D	F
Quality of service you received when purchasing	A	B	C	D	F
Ease of use	A	B	C	D	F
Quality of content	A	B	C	D	F
Page layout	A	B	C	D	F
Organization of material	A	B	C	D	F
Suitability for grade level	A	B	C	D	F
Instructional value	A	B	C	D	F

COMMENTS:_____

_____

What specific supplemental materials would help you meet your current—or future—instructional needs?

_____

Have you used other Walch publications? If so, which ones?_____

May we use your comments in upcoming communications?   ___Yes   ___No

Please **FAX** this completed form to **207-772-3105**, or mail it to:

Product Development, J.Weston Walch, Publisher, P.O. Box 658, Portland, ME 04104-0658

We will send you a **FREE GIFT** as our way of thanking you for your feedback. **THANK YOU!**